At Se

Patrick Dennis

My Madcap Mexican Adventure with the Author of *Auntie Mame*

Robert Karr

Presented by Bernie Ardia

RATTLING GOOD YARNS
PRESS

Rattling Good Yarns Press
33490 Date Palm Drive 3065
Cathedral City CA 92235
USA
www.rattlinggoodyarns.com

Cover Design: Rattling Good Yarns Press

Library of Congress Control Number: 2022947052
ISBN: 978-1-955826-25-9

First Edition

Dedication

Raub Karr
And All Dreamers

Preface

Fate? Happenstance? Karma or Predestination? Perhaps it's Divine Decree or What is written. Possibly it's *The Wheel of Fortune,* or simply "the way the cookie crumbles." Or, in my case, "the way the ball bounces."

None of us can plan the direction our lives take. Yet, even if we arrive close to where we thought we were going, characters can steer us toward new and surprising experiences.

Born in Pasadena makes me a Southern California native. Yes, we exist. Being creative has been a constant in my life. Show business seemed the only path forward.

I was fortunate to have an Auntie Mame in my life. My grandmother. We didn't travel the world together, but travels we certainly had. She opened my eyes to what guided my career, my interests, and gave me a curiosity for people, places, and things, that I still have today.

My grandmother was an award-winning hairstylist. She could do wonders with the type of elegant hairstyles of the 50s, 60s, and 70s that could only be seen in films or magazines. She owned numerous salons and gift shops in Southern California. To me, it seemed like she could turn any idea into reality and switch ideas as fast as they were completed. She always created.

My favorite memories began when I was quite young, on Mondays— salons back then were closed on Mondays. So I got picked up in a beautiful Cadillac, driven by my grandfather, and we headed to Beverly Hills. The classy marble storefronts, and windows displaying the finest goods, made me aware that more could be had in life.

The real reason for these drives into 'the city' was to spy. And spy we did! Very exciting for a young boy.

Because all the salons were closed on Mondays, my grandmother had a route of stops. These included every one of the top salons of the day. As I remember, we would all get out—though my grandfather sometimes stayed behind the wheel with the *Daily Racing Form*. We stood at the windows with our hands up to our faces to cut the glare, as my grandmother studied the latest trends in salon interiors on the West Coast. I'm not sure what I was absorbing, but I think I learned way too much about chandeliers and mirrors. Certainly, 'style' was being taught to me by my Auntie Mame. Sadly, I paid no attention to hairstyles or anything at all to do with hair.

And what have I done for the last forty years? *Hair Design*!

I have created hair designs for countless performers and for many musicals. I have surpassed my goals more than a few times. Like my own Auntie Mame, switching gears to turn a side hobby into a book, *Barbra Streisand in New York City: A Self-Guided Tour of Landmark Locations in the Career of Barbra Streisand*. Life does stay interesting.

I usually look ahead, and I'm far more interested in what's next.

I love to study the past and use it as a foundation for something new and unseen.

My circle of friends has always been a colorful group. Performers, designers, producers, and collectors. These people have made my life larger. Listening to stories of their personal journeys, about the paths that bring us together for whatever reasons, creates wonder and growth.

It's said that LUCK is the intersection of knowledge and opportunity.

During the late Fall of 2020, I received a box of "Things I think you will enjoy reading" from one of my extraordinary friends, Ms. Lori McCormack. There were many folders of photographs of her sister, singer-actress Ann McCormack (Married name, Livermore). Photos of her nephew, actor Don Stroud, signed books she had been given, and a spiral-bound manuscript called *Patrick & Me*.

In the past, I had heard many stories of Lori's writer friend through the years. Stories of their time in our mutually loved Waikiki. Coincidentally, Jerry and Robert "Raub" Karr now lived blocks away from our home in Rancho Mirage. Since the day we called this desert oasis our home, Lori tried to get my husband, Steve, and I, together with Jerry and Raub. "You'll have a ball getting together with those guys," she would exclaim. We tried. A few phone conversations and exchanged emails were as close as we got to meeting them. Unfortunately, Jerry and Raub had health issues at the time, which finally led to Raub's passing in 2017.

Back to the future. Now, three years after Raub's passing, his manuscript, *Patrick & Me,* is on my desk, and I am intrigued. At the time, a world pandemic was going on, and I was too busy to read the manuscript. So, it sat on my desk, looking at me, and I at it. It was when we packed for our annual jaunt to stay in a bungalow at The Beverly Hills Hotel to write Holiday cards (This *is* normal, right?) that I picked up the spiral-bound manuscript and put it in my bag.

By page twelve, I was on the phone with Lori. "Lori," I announced, "This is *really* good!"

She wholeheartedly agreed and continued with more stories of Robert and Jerry in Waikiki and the years beyond. Towards the close of our conversation, I asked, "What is going to happen to this? Is the family going to try and publish it? Who even owns it?"

I just couldn't bear the thought of it sitting in its spiral binder, only being shared with a few people. I was upset by this and hadn't even finished reading it!

Lori couldn't answer my questions, but she promised to give Jerry a call and inquire about it.

I finished reading the manuscript; and loved each chapter more than the last.

It didn't take long before Lori called me back to tell me there were no plans at all for *Patrick & Me.* After a few letters and emails, it was settled. I was blessed with the gift of sharing this incredible tale of a fascinating adventure with Robert, his friend Walter, and the legendary Patrick Dennis, the author of *Auntie Mame*—as well as many more beloved stories.

It was the way the ball bounced. Right into my lap!

I now felt the obligation to rescue this story for those who love adventure, colorful characters, and the kind of true-life story that, when told, nobody will believe!

To me, the story reads visually, like finding an old Polaroid photograph. The kind of photograph that the longer you look at it, the more it reveals.

Andy Warhol said, 'A Polaroid of a time—An experience through a lens."

The incredible American designer Halston said, "Life is like a picture."

This book that you hold in your hands takes me on a visual ride through the lens of a writer, about a writer. I believe it will do the same for you.

In his autobiography, *The Kid Stays in the Picture*, film producer Robert Evans wrote, "There are three sides to every story, your side, my side, and the truth. And no one is lying."

The original title by Robert Karr was:

"I"
Patrick and ~~Me~~

A brilliant title to me as I read the manuscript. However, had his title remained, you probably would not be reading his book.

Robert's original introduction explained so much, and the cleverness of his original idea should not be lost. All a part of the *rescue*.

Robert Karr's Original Introduction:

During my long life, I have thanked God for my thousands of friends, and I can happily say that I could call Patrick Dennis one of them.

Patrick, or in actuality, Edward Everett Tanner, III, was the author of countless books: *Auntie Mame, Around the World with Auntie Mame, Genius, The Joyous Season, Tony, How Firm a Foundation, Guestward Ho!, The Pink Hotel, Little Me, First Lady, Paradise,* and *3-D*. At least, these were the ones he "fessed" up to.

He was vain, married, and ambitious, but terribly insecure. His writing was fabulous with unending ideas. His typing, punctuation, and spelling were highly questionable, but never his usage of grammar. He could write notes to me in a humorous way, "he don't want no more of this" and never give it another thought, but if I typed it the way he wrote it, it took on a new dimension. To Patrick, the "King's English" was the only English.

My title of *Patrick and Me* would be unbearable to Patrick. I was constantly corrected in my speech and typing. Therefore, in honor of "he who is always correct," I corrected my title to read:

"I"

Patrick and ~~Me~~.

Bernie Ardia, 2023, Rancho Mirage, California

Bernie Ardia

Acknowledgements

There were more people in the journey for this book to becoming a reality.

First and foremost, **Jerrold Peterson**: Robert Karr's partner and only by coincidence, my neighbor! He has become a friend that shares a great sense of humor and looks at the world much like myself.

Lori McCormack: One of two surviving women in a most fascinating family. She and her sister **Judy** are as dear to us as their one of a kind sister **Ann McCormack.**

Trudi Licht: the first editor to tackle the spiral bound manuscript and dissect the words within.

My publisher, **Ian Henzel** and the folks at Rattling Good Yarns. His immediate reaction to this work was so similar to mine that I knew this was in the right hands.

St Sukie de la Croix: Who masterfully tackled a challenging edit to a book without an original author who could be consulted. The *rhythm and bite* I felt with my first read, remains.

James Magruder for stepping forward to present a stunning foreword.

Thank you to my husband, **Stephen Jopson,** who has put up with more "I have an idea" than Ricky Ricardo ever heard! Without him, this and many other dreams would never have come true.

I feel extremely lucky to share this story.

Perhaps the characters in one of Patrick Dennis's novels drew you towards this book, or perhaps a colorful witty friend of yours shared it.

Whatever way it came to you, you can call it ... fate.

Foreword

ALMOST TRUE

In 1903, ragtime genius Scott Joplin, who would only find fame a half-century after his death with the cinematic release of *The Sting*, was touring the Midwest with his first opera, *A Guest of Honor*. In Illinois—or Kansas—a company member stole the box office receipts, which left Joplin unable to meet payroll, or to pay for their lodgings. His confiscated belongings, lost forever, included the score to *A Guest of Honor,* which dramatized a White House dinner President Theodore Roosevelt had held for civil rights leader and educator Booker T. Washington in 1901.

In 1922, journalist Ernest Hemingway wired his first wife, Hadley, in Paris, to gather up all his fiction manuscripts, which included a novel he'd written about World War One, and get on a train to join him in Geneva. At the Gare de Lyon, Hadley stepped away for a moment from the suitcase she'd packed. On her return, it had vanished. As had the manuscripts *and* the carbon copies. Hemingway never attempted to rewrite the novel, and would later claim, when in his cups, which was often, that Hadley's lapse of attention was the reason why he divorced her.

Lost (and recovered) luggage, as well as the (chronic) non-payment of bills, are plot features in Robert Karr's *At Sea with Patrick Dennis: My Madcap Mexican Adventure with the Author of Auntie Mame.* I reference the Joplin opera and the Hemingway novel, because Karr's sensationally entertaining memoir was also nearly lost forever. I'll leave the story of its near consignment to a landfill to its savior, Bernie Ardia, and focus on how its current publication by Rattling Good Yarns Press is an act of cultural restitution.

Gay and queer men of my vintage (b. 1960) grew up without the Internet. To join the boys in the band, you had to look for clues, and follow the trail of breadcrumbs from one high or low cultural artifact or icon to another. The acculturation was precise but piecemeal, and seldom positive: Charles Nelson Reilly and Paul Lynde on the game shows. Late-night talk show appearances by Truman Capote, Waylon Flowers and Madame, and Rip Taylor. Rex Reed. Liberace. *The Front Runner* and *Faggots* and *Maurice* and *Dancer from the Dance* and *Giovanni's Room* and *Death in Venice* and *The Lord Won't Mind*. Davis, Crawford, Dietrich, Edward Everett Horton, Don Knotts, Tony Randall, *Cobra Woman, Song of the Loon, The Lion in Winter,* "Notes on Camp," Cole Porter, *A Chorus Line,* Judy and Barbra, and Mabel Mercer and Portia Nelson. *After Dark* magazine, *That Certain Summer,* Ruth Draper, Andy Warhol, Little Richard, *Cruising, Dog Day Afternoon, Sunday, Bloody Sunday,* Elton John, David Bowie, David Hockney, Lance Loud, Paul Cadmus, Ned Rorem, Montgomery Clift, James Dean, and Sal Mineo. Tennessee Williams. Grandfathers Whitman and Wilde. Auden and Britten and Pears, The International Male catalog, The Village People, Cecil Beaton, Noël Coward, Christopher Isherwood, *Myra Breckinridge*, Uncle Charlie on *My Three Sons*, Mr. French on *Family Affair,* and was it true that Rock Hudson and Jim Nabors were secretly married? (Despite my rejection of all things *Gomer Pyle U.S.M.C,* I wanted their love to be true.)

Am I leaving anyone out? (Don't answer that.) Suffice it to say that the combined forces of Bette Midler, Lily Tomlin, Liza Minnelli, Fran Leibowitz, Steven Sondheim, Maggie Smith, Jennifer Holliday, and Keith Haring, not to mention the ever-escalating global catastrophe of AIDS permanently blew the door off the closet by the mid-'80s.

Add Patrick Dennis to my longlist. N/ever heard of him? Neither highbrow nor lowbrow, Patrick Dennis was the *nom de plume* of Edward Everett Tanner III, who was born in Evanston, Illinois, in 1921, and published sixteen comic novels from 1953 to 1972, the first three of them under the pseudonym of Virginia Rowan. He struck gold with his fourth, *Auntie Mame: An Irreverent Escapade.* One would have to compare *Auntie Mame*'s instant success in 1955 to that of Beyoncé dropping her latest album. It spent a record-breaking 112 weeks on the *New York Times* Bestseller List. Success begets success: playwrights Jerome Lawrence and Robert E. Lee turned *Auntie Mame* into a stage vehicle for screen star Rosalind Russell. It opened on Broadway while the book was still selling a thousand copies a day and ran for 639 performances before closing at the end of June in 1958, with Beatrice

Lillie now in the title role, Russell having left the show in April to make the film version. Released that same December, after the publication of Dennis' fictional follow-up, *Around the World with Auntie Mame,* the movie was a critical triumph and a box-office success, as well as an entry point into the material for gay men living outside of New York—at least until 1966 when...

Mame, the musical, opened at the Winter Garden Theatre. Lawrence and Lee had adapted their play version, and Jerry Herman, fresh off of his first "Big Lady" show, *Hello, Dolly!* (1964), wrote the score, which included several piano bar classics, among them the ballad "If He Walked into My Life," "Open a New Window," "It's Today," "We Need a Little Christmas," and the witchy-bitchy "Bosom Buddies." The title torch was passed from Roz Russell to Angela Lansbury, who won her first of four Leading Actress in a Musical Tony Awards and, given how strenuous the role was, sometimes passed out in her dressing room during intermission. Celeste Holm, Ann Miller, Jane Morgan, and Janis Page succeeded Lansbury in the part.

The 1974 film version of *Mame* starred Lucille Ball through Vaseline-smeared camera lenses. Considered the worst stage-to-film musical transfer ever, until *Cats* in 2019, it finally killed the franchise. (It is hoped that Dennis, who died of pancreatic cancer in 1976, never saw it.) To date, the play has never had a Broadway revival (its cast is enormous); and although show queens are incessantly recasting the Big Lady in the Broadway chatrooms (Cher, Streep, Gaga, Beyoncé), Lansbury herself only managed to run a month in an under-advertised revival in the summer of 1983.

Yet Auntie Mame's oft-quoted philosophy—"Life is a banquet, and most poor suckers are starving to death!" and Dennis' captivating portrayal of glamorous, high-life New York and its people between the World Wars are an evergreen lure to the generations of gay men who have followed the trail via the book, the movie, and/or the musical. But here's the thing: Dennis was resolutely middlebrow; his works reached a mass audience; although he slept with men, he was a devoted father of two, and until his death, remained married to Louise Stickney, whom he'd wed at the age of 27; although shot through with a sensibility, a certain *tone,* if you will, that today practically shrieks lavender, *Auntie*

Mame is hardly a coterie artifact. Everyone who encounters her wishes for his/her/their own magical Auntie Mame to show them how to live. If alive today, Dennis might be out and proud—or he might just as easily identify somewhere else along the gender spectrum.

I might now wax about the history of comic novels, from Jane Austen to *Zuleika Dobson*, but will not, as my list would exceed the roster of gay icons and artifacts with which I've previously taxed your patience. Let's just say that in the matter of Patrick Dennis, whose work goes by the outdated publishing category of "light fiction," P.G. Wodehouse, E.F. Benson, Evelyn Waugh, and to a lesser extent, Carl Van Vechten and Ronald Firbank, are his literary forebears. His current descendants would include Armistead Maupin and Carl Hiassen, and the female-centered beach reads of Jennifer Wiener and Elin Hilderbrand.

Light fiction is meant to entertain the way a stage farce does. It is not mean-spirited, and it doesn't punish. Instead, it relies on plot contrivances and coincidences, mistaken identities and aliases, behavioral tics and repetitions, fixed characterizations, improbable romantic inclinations, a supporting cast of utter oddballs, and endowed props. It features a narrative eye that delights in exaggeration and absurdity, a lexicon that favors the unusual word choice (e.g., "portly" or "rubicund," rather than "heavy" or "ruddy"), and a breezy, bemused tone that suggests that no matter how weighed down the characters might become by the vicissitudes of plot and circumstance, everything will turn out right in the end. Order is comically restored. The check clears. No one dies. The luggage is found. There is a non-stop flight home. God and His mysterious ways stay out of the picture.

The subtitle for *Auntie Mame*—"An Irreverent Escapade"—is an apt description for *At Sea with Patrick Dennis: My Madcap Mexican Adventure with the Author of Auntie Mame*. It is a caper that could have been written by Dennis himself. Sometime in the mid-1960s, Robert Karr, known as Raub to his friends (and in the memoir), embarks on the *S.S. Caprice* for a 21-day pleasure cruise from Seattle to Mexico. Accompanying him is Walter Healy, a Felix Unger type when it comes to his outfits. In fact, Walter's sartorial fastidiousness is one of the great running gags of the memoir.

From the very first page: In our mid-twenties, each weighing about 160 pounds and standing six feet tall. Wearing the same size clothing, we often traded and switched sweaters and Levi's. We had lived together in Hawaii for several years...

Hmmm. Roommates, but not lovers? Their cabin has twin beds. Raub's silence throughout the book about their bond is curious; but for a very occasional reference to male hookups, the memoir, like a pre-Stonewall Dennis novel, is completely queer, but utterly chaste. I think it adds to the charm of the book.

At their first port of call, San Francisco, Raub and Walter head to Juanita's Gallery, a decommissioned paddlewheel ferryboat nightspot harbored in Sausalito, where the clientele is, as they used to say, "mixed." There they meet the tall, dapper Roger Danbury, a shipmate who seems to know everything about them already. They make it back to the *Caprice* in the nick of time, and the adventures really begin. Danbury, of course, is Patrick Dennis.

Walter and Dennis jump ship for different reasons in Mexico, and, in the way of some drunken benders, twenty-one days somehow becomes two years. The unlikely *trio de amigos* wander the country by foot, bus, or car, fall in and out with each other, split up, then miraculously reunite in unsavory brothels and high-end hotels from one end of the country to another: Mazatlan, Puerto Vallarta, Acapulco, Oaxaca, San Miguel de Allende, Mexico City. Dennis has a typewriter, and boxes of autographed copies of his works to flatter his way out of scrapes. When his bar bill gets too high, which is nearly always, Walter clips tourists and natives alike with a shell and pea game. Raub maintains his sober good nature and generally plays the straight man, the ideal perspective for describing a dizzying array of secondary characters: Juanita the restaurateur, society ladies false and true, horrid grandchildren, oafish ship pursers, harlots high and low, chiseling hotel managers, heroes on the *Mini-Estrella* midget wrestling circuit, and a rich gay couple by the names of Roberto and Al Jahiz.

Dennis sporadically writes his next book on Roger Danbury's purloined typewriter; money is wired from Dennis' literary agents and quickly spent; Walter loses most of his wardrobe, lets his hair grow long—it is the sixties, after all—and gets deeply tan. Millions more cocktails are consumed before the trio finally breaks up for good. Like Ulysses before him, Raub discovers there comes a time for home again, home again, jiggety jig.

As we know, truth is stranger than fiction. Because *At Sea with Patrick Dennis* is a memoir, and not a work of light fiction, it is granted permission to have a serious ending. When he finally left Mexico, Patrick Dennis reinvented himself one final time; he lived in San Diego and worked as a butler named Tanner to Joan Kroc, wife of Roy Kroc, the founder, and CEO of McDonald's. As his health declined, he revealed his true identity to his boss, and was flown home to be with Louise and his children, Michael and Betsy, in New York, where he died in his sleep on November 6, 1976.

All that the world has learned in the half-century since Dennis' death about manic depression, ADHD, and alcoholism cannot diminish the shine or still the laughter in Raub's memoir of unforgettable friendship. A gay man of my vintage (b.1960) cannot help but pine for that far-off time before GPS and Venmo, when three knights errant could wander by the seats of their pants *untracked* for two years, bickering, often hungover, sometimes penniless, in a foreign country. The best books make you homesick for places you have never been—so it is with *At Sea with Patrick Dennis.* Enjoy.

James Magruder has published four works of fiction, the most recent being *Vamp Until Ready* (Rattling Good Yarns Press, 2021) and written the books for two Broadway musicals, *Triumph of Love,* and the Sir Philip Sidney/Go-Go's blank verse mashup, *Head Over Heels.*

"I always start writing with a clean piece of paper and a dirty mind."
—**Patrick Dennis**

Chapter one
Walter, the Soigné

My God, in a few months, it will be coming up to the half-century anniversary of the first time I ever spoke to the character that would forever change my life. His name was Patrick Dennis. It was during one of those terrible so-many-days-at-sea adventurous trips to Mexico: leaving Seattle, to San Francisco, Los Angeles, Mazatlan, and finally, our furthest point south, Acapulco—the rumored city of sin, where fellow travelers engaged in excessive drink, wild sex, exotic Mexican food, and new strange people.

The time of year was early spring with the usual foul weather in Seattle. The rain and snow caused white-haired ladies to drive with extreme caution during their afternoon visits to Nordstrom's, Frederick & Nelson's, and Best Apparel—where my fellow traveling partner, Walter Healy, was personnel director. In the 1960s, the women were more fashionable and wore hats and gloves as they drove their personal cars to a bridge game or shopping session downtown.

Each woman driver considered herself an expert in navigating icy roads on the possibly semi-bald tires of her automobile, up and down the ramping streets of smooth concrete roadways and ancient cobblestone inlaid bricks. The roads had been paved with worn cobblestones on the downhill streets in the center of downtown. Cars slide sideways with bewildered lady drivers clutching their steering wheels with both gloved hands. A look of absolute terror froze on their faces as the heavy automobile slid sideways into cars parked along the road's edge. This made Seattle an insurance man's paradise with wealthy clients and lots of afternoon "outings" for the wives.

Walter and I had been planning this trip for several months. In our minds, each day of rain that fell on the city of Seattle added another five days before the official departure date. As the sailing date grew closer, so did Walter's extensive packing of luggage for the 21-day cruise.

The steamship company agreed upon and suggested that each passenger be allotted one suitcase per person in writing. Our stateroom on the ship, the SS Caprice, was small—so small, in fact, one had to step over the end of a single bed to enter the lavatory. With two beds in the room, the bathroom door was unable to fully open.

We both commented, "Gee what do fat people do to get to the bathroom?"

Walter and I were in our mid-twenties, each weighing about 160 pounds and standing six feet tall. Wearing the same size clothing, we often traded and switched sweaters and Levi's. We had lived together in Hawaii for several years, where Walter had been employed in a formal office setting. Being in the broadcasting industry, my wardrobe in the islands tended to be more on the casual Hawaiian side.

Walter's clothing collection was extensive and always pristinely relegated to each item's proper clothes hanger, positioned in his closet first by the item (i.e., trousers: black to the right and lighter colors in varying degrees to the left). Also, he was most insistent that the hangers be evenly spaced on the hanging rod with no hanger being allowed to touch another. Walter never wore the same shirt twice before being laundered. His dry-cleaning bills would have provided food on the table for a family of four for a week. He owned seven suits, six sports coats, and a collection of over forty neckties. His laundered dress shirts were meticulously ironed, hung on a hanger, and again arranged by the darkest color to the right and the lighter to the left. His entire weekend would be ruined if one pair of his ten pairs of leather shoes was not returned from the shoe-repair shop polished and ready for its designated shoetree. I won't even mention the dress-sock situation other than to say that two complete dresser drawers were allocated to his sock collection. All laundered, properly folded and arranged by color. You've got it—the darks on the right and the lights to the left.

The preparation of Walter's suitcase for the ocean voyage began exactly four weeks before our departure date. His bed was artfully covered with possible clothing selections from his vast collection. Chairs held underwear and socks, all perfectly color coordinated.

Walter had covered my bed with a clean sheet over the ruffed-up linens and blankets. Where I slept became a platform for Walter's "casual" clothing. The proper necktie was draped around the collar of the finely starched shirt on its hanger. Trousers, with belts coiled in a circle like rattlesnakes ready to strike, were the base foundation on his bed. Appropriate shoes were lined up like soldiers with the proper color socks draped over the shoetrees. Everything was on display, and two plastic containers of safety pins were required to attach labels to the item, identifying that article as belonging to Selection Number 1 through 46. Walter was now ready to determine his wardrobe for each day on the twenty-one days at sea. Group Number 1 was to be worn on the day of departure. Number 2 was for the first night onboard and into the dining room—second seating, of course. Number 3 was the first morning for breakfast, followed by a tour of the ship's facilities. Number 4 was that day's lunch. Number 5 was the afternoon cocktail-hour array, and so the numbers progressed.

Walter's secretary at Best's Apparel had typed a master dressing list. I'm sure it became the subject of great conversation during the secretary's lunch break with the other employees.

Some of the numbered groupings were used twice, subject to close inspection of wrinkled shirts and changes of socks. These numbered groups were the days we were allowed off the ship for touring visits into the various Mexican towns at the assigned dockings.

In total, Walter arrived on board the SS Caprice with not just one but four new suitcases, which once emptied of their contents, were stacked one inside of the other. I considered my two pairs of Levi's, a few shirts, two pairs of trousers, one belt, and two pairs of shoes perfectly adequate for the time at sea and the Mexican countryside.

The sailing voyage began in Seattle, and the stops in San Francisco and Los Angeles were for only part of the day. One could leave the ship, but there wasn't much to see on our first stop, other than the Port of San Francisco, Walter's hometown, a quick lunch, or an early evening cocktail at one of Walter's once-favorite bars.

Our three meals a day were provided by the steamship company. The SS Caprice was large, and our cabin was on the port side, in the mid-range of the economy-priced rooms. We had both been pre-approved for a credit line at any of the ship's bars and nightclubs. We soon found that the extravagant nightclub show was hackneyed with singers who were well beyond their prime in performing the modern music of the day. A dance couple who, after executing a series of Veloz and Yolanda tricky dance steps—with much lifting in the air and deep bending—ventured out into the audience. There, they enticed poor unsuspecting ocean travelers to become their partners on the dance floor.

The orchestra, totaling five elderly and overweight musicians, sat and played with no expression, each musical number they attempted. The ensemble consisted of a piano/organ player, a trumpet/trombone player, a guitar/clarinet player, the string bass player—also in charge of lighting changes, as well as acting as the emcee—and lastly, the drummer. He was a midget of a man dressed in a faded light powder-blue tuxedo, a pink ruffled tuxedo shirt with white socks inside his matching pink shoes. He sat behind the largest drum set I had ever seen. He had not one but two large bass drums. Usually, the stretch drum skin is white and non-transparent. His was a glistening clear plastic that allowed the audience to witness his bouncing leg movements to every beat of the music. His right foot switched back and forth from one large bass drum to the other, while his left moved in time up and down on the cymbal rack, which volume-wise seemed to be his favorite percussion instrument. Practically every beat of the orchestra's music was accented with a loud crash of his cymbal. Flickering lights responded to each "boom" emitted from either one of the bass drums, the snap of the snare drum with his sticks, or the sizzle of his wire brushes. It was with the cymbals that a red flashing light lit up the interior of each bass drum. On the first evening, we asked the waitress if she could mention that the drums were "a little too loud." She replied, "Yah, we know, but he's the leader of the orchestra and won't do anythin' about it. Lotsa people complain. I can move your table if you wanna."

We stayed long enough to witness Veloz and Yolanda startle a husband-and-wife by dragging them forcibly onto the dance floor and executing the tango, foxtrot, waltz, boogie-woogie, and a cha-cha-cha.

The audience husband-and-wife team, chosen to be the evening's *danseur* and *danseuse* by Veloz and Yolanda, were probably from a farming area in mid-state Washington or Oregon, well into their Social Security pension days, but willing to participate in this dazzling bit of show biz fun.

The husband sported a brown, heavy wool suit, probably purchased many years ago from JC Penny, thick-soled scuffed brown Oxfords, and a white shirt with large gaudy cuff links. Yolanda clutched his hand in a "no-refusal" stranglehold as she propelled him onto the dance floor. She swirled several turns before him, leaned suggestively back against his shoulder, and executed a loving glance into his terrified eyes.

Veloz, obviously more senior in experience than Yolanda, was having trouble getting the farmer's wife to leave the safety and security of her once comfortable dining chair. Veloz masterly flourished a flamenco step in his shiny black dance shoes and fell to his knees before the startled woman. He kissed her hand and convinced her to join him on the dance floor next to Yolanda and the farmer husband, who still wore a look of absolute terror on his face.

The farmer's wife suddenly acquiesced to the begging demands of Veloz. She bolted upright to step from behind the dining table, exposing one of the largest sets of hips on a woman I had ever witnessed. When seated, the woman, hidden within her demure silk evening dress, gave no sign or suggestion of her possessing such an enormous *derriere*. Sadly, after being seated at the table during the earlier show, a portion of her flowery printed silk-like dress had lodged itself in the upper band of her panties. The effect was a rakish exposure of fleshy, corpulent skin. Her stout thighs and legs cascaded into her tiny high heel shoes.

Veloz struck a pose to begin the tango, and the music started. Then, with a gale of laughter, the farmwife bent forward and clutched her hands over her giggling mouth.

For those of us unfortunate enough to witness her forward bend, the full display of her bulbous posterior jammed into bright pink panty underwear was *the* highlight of the entire evening.

It was apparent that the farm couple didn't know any of the dances proposed by Veloz and Yolanda. Then they, after embarrassing the couple, departed the dance floor silently with much bowing and blowing of kisses to the audience. Finally, they slithered behind the stage curtains, leaving the farmer and his wife alone in center stage. The orchestra started a romping version of "Charleston, Charleston" as the farm couple executed a feverish leg-kicking rendition of the dance to the full applause of the audience.

Our first evening dinner aboard the ship was scheduled for the second seating, as would be for all our meals. We had requested a table for two, not wanting to be saddled with obnoxious types. Still, it became clear that the deuce tables were in the center of the room and evident to the other diners. So instead, we elected to join a woman and her grandson, sharing a table for four, away from the glaring chandelier lights and dance floor.

The woman was Edith Winton and her 14-year-old grandson, David.

Mrs. Edith Winton and her Grandson

David had one of those unnerving personalities that either made you want to slap his smart-aleck face or totally avoid anything he did or said. Walter and I chose the latter, avoiding him entirely even when he asked us a direct question.

"Hush, David, Grannie's talking to the two nice gentlemen, and we don't use those kinds of words in public. Now eat your dinner and sit still."

David was fully aware that his grandmother adored him and lavished countless gifts upon him during the year. He was also treated to what she called "their vacation together." The vacation was anywhere he wanted to go, as long as it was by ship. Edith suffered greatly from claustrophobia and was unable to fly in airplanes. Walking through the interior hallways of the ship, she was forced to walk in the exact center of the long hall. She had booked the most expensive suite available on the ship, including an adjoining separate bedroom-bath for David, a small kitchenette, a bar, and a spacious living room with large sliding glass doors leading to a private lanai area at the most forward bow of the ship.

David, who was never criticized or taught any manners by his parents, was allowed to run from one end of the ship to the other, free of any scolding or reprimands by the crew. Mrs. Winton was a widow and now held the majority shares of common stock in the company that owned the SS Caprice and five other steamships.

Everyone was aware that Mr. Winton had been very wealthy when he died, except Mrs. Winton.

Being constantly in the company of Mrs. Winton, Walter and I were ceremoniously greeted by ship personnel and especially the captain, Jonathan Cartwright III—a most old "salt of the sea" character as one could imagine. I questioned the extent of the captain's experience on a large vessel, as his constant reply to questions posed to him from his crew was, "Take care of that for me, would you?"

Captain Cartwright was determined to win over the friendship of Mrs. Winton and her grandson, no matter what. This was his first sailing with Mrs. Winton as his most esteemed passenger. He had assembled an able crew who had been ordered to support the captain in his venture. A flow of fresh flowers arrived each morning to her stateroom as well as our dining table for each meal, courtesy of the captain, or at least that was the name credited on the card.

Mrs. Winton slept late each morning while David dressed, entered the galley kitchen of any of the several eating locations aboard the ship, and took whatever he desired. Sometimes he removed food from fellow passengers' plates in the dining room. While crude and intruding on his fellow travelers, his stealing food was never censured by the staff. If a complaining fellow passenger spoke in protest to David, the contemptible juvenile would upset food plates onto their lap.

A security officer was stationed 24-hours a day on the ladder steps leading to the crew's quarters, engine room, and ship's laundry. Certain areas had been posted as "off limits" to David by Captain Cartwright, who was well informed of the mischief David could create. Not only was David stealing from employees' lockers, but he also switched the contents of sugar and salt containers in the food locker bins. One morning, he coated the steel ladder steps to the boiler room with gallons of maple syrup.

Four junior officers of the ship were assigned to offer apologies, free dry cleaning of garments, complimentary dining experiences, and credits in any bar on board. In one case, Mrs. Winton offered a couple an all-expenses-paid vacation on another company ship. She also refunded the costs of their original ticket after David vandalized their stateroom. Besides a brief lecture from Mrs. Winton, David's punishment was his confinement for the afternoon in their suite.

The second evening aboard the SS Caprice, we churned our way toward San Francisco as we weathered a rainstorm and high waves. It allowed Walter and me to get to know Edith, or "Edie," as she wanted to be called. David was not feeling well. He was seasick. And as Edie put it, "His poor little tummy is all upset." The rocking waves plus the gallons of ice cream he stole from the snack bar put him in his bed for the night.

Walter and I thought that the unlikable and despicable little snot had it coming. Still, we cooed our feigned concern for his health to Edie, who promised to report our interest in his well-being to the little boy.

Being only three at our table was delightful. Walter asked Edie to dance following the salad course. Edie had previously ordered our dinners and insisted it was her treat for the evening. Any specialty item over and above the listed main entrée was an additional charge to our bill from the ship.

Our entrée for the evening was giant Alaskan king crab legs. The head chef had been warned that this expensive selection would be served to Mrs. Winton's table as three silver serving carts appeared out of nowhere, filled with chipped ice and enough crab legs to feed Napoleon's army.

A spectacle of white-coated cooks appeared, pushing a massive stainless steel serving table covered with a huge copper bowl, whisks, containers of extra virgin olive oil, eggs neatly stacked like one of the giant pyramids of ancient Egypt, woven baskets of fresh lemons, and one of the tallest glass carafe bottles filled with sparkling vinegar. Two cooks began expertly cracking the eggs and separating the yolks from the whites. Their striking of the eggshell against the copper bowl, deftly dividing the two shell halves, was in perfect timing with the music played by the orchestra. Next, the slippery egg whites were allowed to cascade from one shell to another. The arm movements of the two chefs were synchronized and lofty. Finally, with the whites all placed in one bowl and yolks in another, it was time to whisk.

The master chef, a mustached elderly man, strolled majestically to the table, inspected the previous work that had been done, and grasped his stainless-steel whisk. A single light spotlighted the opacity of the bass drum skins. It accented the orchestra leader in his pink shirt and shoes. The drummer began a drum roll as the whisk entered the copper bowl, and gigantic strokes whipped and smashed the yolks in a fury of smoothness. An open flame from a Sterno heater cast blue flashes of light. They gently warmed the exterior of the copper bowl before it was once again held in the crooked arm of the master chef. He grasped it firmly against his large chest, like a father clutching his favorite son around the shoulders. The whisk flashed high in the air, first showing the bright orange of the egg yolks. After a counted number of rapid whisk strokes, the mixture was again lifted high into the air above the copper bowl. It had magically turned to a thick lemon color for the audience to see. There was a wave of "aahs" from the chef's captive audience.

Next, an assistant measured and prepared the flavoring for the concoction: a dash of vinegar from the tall carafe; then, bright yellow lemons were rolled vigorously against the surface of the stainless-steel table, sliced in half, covered with a bright yellow straining cloth, and squeezed of their strong acidic juice.

White pepper was sifted with dry yellow mustard and blended into the vinegar and lemon juice, then slowly incorporated into the stiffened egg yolks.

The dining room was silent except for the occasional whisk of the stainless steel against the copper bowl and the snare drum snapping.

The master chef, satisfied his creation was being correctly done, handed the copper bowl to another assistant and stuck his index finger into the mixture to extract a sample for tasting. The second and third assistant, in turn, inserted their fingers for a sampling. Not a word was spoken between the three men, their tall mushroom-shaped hats tilted on their heads. There was a knowing glance from the master chef as he pinched the correct amount of salt into the bowl, and the mixing continued.

The only female chef in the group stood proudly on a small step stool holding the long-necked oil container. The master chef continued to hold the large copper bowl as assistant number two assumed the duties of the whisk. This time the strokes were even and always in the same direction within the bowl.

The orchestra drum roll converged into the opening of a marching band cadence.

"Varoom!"

"Varoom!"

"Varoom, boom boom!"

"Varoom!"

"Varoom!"

"Varoom, boom boom!"

Counted drops of the oil were poured from the thin neck of the oil container by the female chef. The person manning the whisk was not allowed to stop or alter his tempo in his movement of the whisk.

The master chef ducked under the vigorous whisking arm of the now tiring assistant chef. His whisk taking over the exact motion and rhythm. The assistant chef stepped backward, proudly displaying his whisk, thick with the lemon-white substance.

Drop by drop, the oil was added.

"Varoom!"

"Varoom!"

"Varoom, boom boom!"

The orchestra struck up the opening bars of "La Marseillaise," the French National Anthem.

Worldly travelers dining that night rested their eating utensils, folded their dinner napkins, and stood in silence upon hearing the first notes of the anthem. Slowly other diners rose to stand at attention as if they understood the music or the significance of what was happening. Finally, the master chef again inserted his index finger into the mixture, tasted the white/yellow mixture, and shouted, *"Voila! La mayonnaise, c'est la perfection absolue!"*

That evening the captain honored our table with a sampling of the masterly made mayonnaise and a taste of the Alaskan king crab. He also earned points with Edie Winton by announcing that the ship's doctor had reported that David was fast asleep in his bedroom. At least, he was supposed to be—the poor young lady babysitting him had not been told that David had his own entrance in and out of his private bedroom.

"I am sorry, Mrs. Winton, that the rough sea has made poor Master David ill. We are anticipating higher waves at the end of the first watch," the obliging captain said. "For you land lovers," addressing his remarks to Walter and me, "That's the shift prior to midnight tonight."

Walter, having enjoyed his usual complement of martinis and several glasses of an excellent fine wine, responded to the captain, "Oh, come now, Captain, would you say the increase will be at six, seven, or eight bells? Can't you be a little more specific?"

Finishing our dinners, we made our excuses to the captain and guided Mrs. Winton to her stateroom. For some reason, the evening's abundance of fine wines and cocktails had diminished her malaise of claustrophobia. She practically galloped to her suite, swinging a token sampling of Alaska king crab at her side for David in case he was still awake.

The young doctor's assistant was fast asleep on the sofa, and the room was flooded with light. Edie knocked softly on David's bedroom door, but she received no answer from within. Finally, concerned, she entered to find David's bed empty. He was nowhere to be found.

Frantic telephone calls to the ship's operator and the bridge produced a bevy of junior officers and the captain, all shouting and talking at once. No one had seen David, and an extensive search of the entire ship was ordered. Passengers were rudely awakened from their sleep and questioned if they had seen the boy. Off-duty crew members were pressed back into service. Doors banged as every inch of the SS Caprice was searched.

Several of the first-class passengers, unaware of what was happening, placed their life jackets on over their bedroom clothing expecting the ship to sink at any moment, á la the Titanic.

The SS Caprice sat dead calm in the pitch-black Pacific Ocean's waters for hours. Massive searchlights flooded the waves in search of the missing boy. The captain ordered that the sounding of the eerie foghorn be blown every few minutes in the hopes that the missing David might hear the sound and yell out his location. If he were, indeed, in the choppy black ocean water.

During this confusion, a mid-shipman spotted a whiff of smoke rising from the forward bow lanai of Mrs. Winton's suite. Security officers and a fire brigade were dispersed to all areas of the cabins on the top deck.

David was returned to the loving arms of his grandmother. She refused to believe that her grandson would set fire to anything, let alone the lanai furniture of her suite. The incident was recorded and closed in the ship's log. Everyone was given permission to return to their beds.

Chapter Two
The First Port of Call–San Francisco

The following morning was ablaze with sunlight. The sea was once again calm. Luckily our cabin had a port-side window, so we caught glimpses of the northern California coastline.

As Walter so pompously pointed out, we would arrive at the Port of San Francisco shortly after 2:00 pm or during the afternoon watch of four bells. I trusted his knowledge of ships' bells and watches but still relied upon my trusty Timex for the correct time. I never completely mastered the numbers of military time: 14:00 hours for 2:00 pm, indeed!

The closer we came to San Francisco, the cloudier and more impaired the weather became. Finally, Captain Cartwright announced over the loudspeaker that the ship had made up the lost time after being "still" in the ocean for the two-hour search for young Master David. "The weather forecast does not look too promising for those who wish to venture into the city. SS Caprice umbrellas are available for those wishing to borrow one. For those of you landlubbers who are planning on going into the city, let me warn you that the SS Caprice sails promptly at eight bells. That's midnight. You must be onboard, or we go without ya!" He shouted his final comments with a no-nonsense tone in his voice. He was not kidding about sailing without a negligent passenger.

After lunch, which we enjoyed without David and his grandmother, we retired to our cabin so Walter could assemble his wardrobe for our excursion into San Francisco. I was warned to select something smart from my meager, unpacked clothing that was still crammed in my one old suitcase.

Walter had commandeered the only closet in our room, all six drawers of the built-in dresser near the bathroom door, and the entire storage space for suitcases in the open space above the closet. His shoes with companion-selected socks and shoetrees covered the writing desk. My old Samsonite suitcase plus two pairs of Walter's most refined Oxfords on top was relegated to under the desk.

The SS Caprice was about to dock, and Walter had still not decided what to wear. It required another hour for him to choose group #12 for the ten-hour outing into the city.

A sympathetic cabin boy took pity on Walter and borrowed a wooden coat rack from the officers' quarters. Carefully positioned in the far corner of our shrinking room, the rack held four of his suits, two sports jackets, and two pairs of matching trousers.

I felt comfortable and appropriately dressed in my only sports jacket, gray sharp-pleated trousers, black shoes with gray socks, my black belt, and a white shirt with striped collegiate tie. Walter stepped out of the steaming bathroom. There were small dabs of toilet paper, with faint traces of blood, on his nicked chin. The tiny porthole window in the bathroom, plus the electric ceiling fan, provided the only circulation in the room. Walter perspired profusely.

"You're wearing that?" he demanded.

"And what's wrong with what I'm wearing?" I barked back.

"You look like some college kid, struggling to finish his last year at junior college or trade school. That's what you look like."

"So sorry, but this is it. You can walk behind me if you like, or we can even take separate taxicabs."

"You know perfectly well that I was planning on wearing ensemble #12 today. That's a navy-blue, custom-tailored jacket, gray slacks, and my black Florsheim wingtips. And that tie! Good God, select one from my collection. The blue stripe interferes with the blue in your shabby-looking jacket. Did you purposely roll your sport jacket up in a bundle for some reason? Garments, especially sport jackets, are to be laid flat in the bottom of the suitcase. Both arms folded over tissue paper, and the tail of the jacket folded back up over the top of the jacket. If I hadn't been with you the evening the waiter spilled food on your jacket, I would accuse you of having rolled the filthy thing up around an Italian salami. Didn't you even think to have it cleaned before we departed on this trip?"

Walter's tone of voice was getting edgy, as was my temper. I had no intention of mentioning that he controlled the entire closet, coat rack, and every available flat surface ... and simply shrugged it off. "Well, at least it will be dark, and Juanita's will be packed to the rafters with people looking like you anyway."

"Qu'avez-vous dit?"

"Oh, you know exactly what I meant. You look as fussily overdressed as you always did, even in Hawaii. Besides, I can't be seen in an ensemble with the same color as yours. I'll make another selection. I don't want someone saying, 'Look, it's Laura Lee Hope's *The Bobbsey Twins*."

"At least *I'll* be dressed like a gentleman. You'll forgive me if I digress and call you Nan or Flossie all evening."

I caught my reflection in the mirror and judged that I didn't look *that* bad. I told Walter that I would meet him on the main deck near the gangplank to go ashore. "I'll be the one talking to the old man without any legs, holding his tin cup up in the air. I don't know if I really want to be seen with you on these precious streets of your San Francisco, especially if you're going to wear a pink outfit."

This time away from Walter gave me the chance to do an assessment of my fellow travelers. As we suspected, the dancing couple from the floor show with Veloz and Yolanda were typical of everyone else on board. It was early spring, the weather in the far northern-seaboard states was still bitterly cold, and school was still in session. Our fellow travelers were mainly older hard-working couples with an "air" of agriculture about them.

The men wore parka jackets, a few with only a tee-shirt underneath, an open-collared flannel shirt, or a thick sweater. The ladies wore their customary dull winter coats. Some women wore slacks, and one debonair beauty sported a newly-bleached head of blond hair and Alaskan fur boots. But, of course, no one was entering a fashion contest. The only purpose was to see something of the city of San Francisco in the brief time allotted. And to be warm while doing it.

A light misty rain began to fall. Several women covered their newly-permed, purple-tinted hair with thin silk scarves. The line for disembarking moved slowly down the gangplank to the wooden dock. The pier was in the Embarcadero District—the edge of the business/financial area, and a good twenty blocks away from the city's downtown area. The major highway, #101, had to be crossed to reach Market or Mission streets. The elevated crosswalk high above the highway was a metal-caged tunnel for the departing passengers to safely reach the city streets.

Walter arrived precisely one hour and twenty minutes later, looking like Mr. Brooks Brothers.

"Where's your winter coat?" he demanded. "You're going to freeze without one, especially when we get to Fisherman's Wharf. Didn't you bring an umbrella? Now we'll have to take taxicabs everywhere, and so help me God, Raub, you can pay for them."

Walter was in a snit, and people began staring at us. Or, more correctly, at my roommate, fellow traveler, Walter, the fashion plate. All he needed was a silver-tipped cane and a monocle over one eye.

He was wearing his black lightweight "funeral" suit, as he called it, complete with a four-point folded handkerchief in the breast pocket. Also, his black wing-tipped leather shoes, a majestic white and gray pin-striped dress shirt with a brilliant red tie expertly knotted, his heavy gray winter-wool coat and a tri-color Hermes silk neck scarf around his neck. His leather-handled black umbrella was draped from the crook of his arm as he donned his light gray doeskin tailored gloves deftly on each hand.

Walter proceeded down the gangplank, and I followed, basking in the splendor of his outrageous fashion attire.

"If the rain increases you may walk next to me, under my umbrella, but I cannot help you in the warmth department," Walter said. "Come on, we can get a taxicab on the other side."

Walter would say it was after 4:00 pm in the afternoon, or first dog watch. It was Friday, and offices and major department stores in San Francisco were still open for business. The sun was fading in the west, and storefronts began to light up and display their window merchandise.

"There's a taxicab stand around the corner here on Market!" Walter shouted above the traffic noise.

"What about taking a cable car to wherever we're going?" I asked.

"Oh, do be sensible, Raub. You would fit right in, riding with all those tourists, but unless you found a seat inside, you'd freeze to death with all the cold wind on your face. The best position to ride in a cable car is the seat next to the car conductor, but only in the dead of winter. In the summer, you would want to be hanging out over the edge of the streetcar to catch the breeze."

We hailed a taxicab and piled into the back seat. Walter commented on the condition and cleanliness of the plastic-covered seat as he barked a destination to the Chinese driver.

Walter requested "The Mark Hopkins Hotel." We saw the driver's face peering into the rear-view mirror, displaying his Asian eyes and missing-tooth grin.

"Ni Hao! Chop-chop. Marky Hopkins," ordered Walter.

"Don't 'chop-chop' or 'Marky Hopkins' me, or you can get another cab," the angry driver retorted. "My name's Herman Wo, and my family's been here since the Gold Rush. Hell, I even went to Presidio High."

I apologized to Herman Wo as Walter continued to inspect the plastic seat covers for dirt and grime.

"The plastic's clean. It's just the cheap fabric underneath that's soiled. Damn drunks," said Mr. Wo, the cab driver.

Oncoming automobile headlights highlighted the steady downpour of rain as we pulled up under the hotel's porte-cochere. I paid the fare and gave Herman Wo a $5 tip to smooth out Walter's insults. We were now about to enter the lobby of the famed Mark Hopkins.

It was magnificent in every detail. A uniformed doorman held open the brass-encased doors for us, and a young bellhop took Walter's umbrella. "May I, Sir?" he asked as he closed the umbrella and banged it against a black plastic canister to dislodge any remaining raindrops. His small white-gloved hands wiped the umbrella with a large, luxurious white towel monogrammed with "MH" on one corner. "Gentlemen, I am sorry, but the afternoon tea has finished at the Top of the Mark, but we have several cafes, restaurants, and bars open at this time, including the Vista Bar on the 19th floor. May I check your coat and umbrella?"

Walter peeled off his gray doeskin gloves, then slipped them into the pockets of his heavy winter coat, along with his Hermes scarf. The bellboy assisted him in removing his coat and presented the items to the woman at the coat-check counter.

Walter casually strolled to the brass filigreed elevator. At the same time, I remained in place with palm extended, anticipating a claim ticket for our belongings.

"Oh, no need for a claim ticket, sir. I will remember you most certainly, and your belongings will be safe."

Thinking 'how grand,' I joined Walter to wait in front of the elevator doors.

At this moment, I noticed something about Walter's appearance that produced a silly deep-down laugh within me.

Annoyed at my giggle, Walter demanded, "What is the matter with you? Behave yourself, we're in the Mark Hopkins Hotel for God's sake."

"Well, la-de-dah. You better walk quickly to the closest men's restroom you can find, or you're going to be the laughingstock of your precious Mark Hopkins Hotel."

Annoyed and confused, Walter entered the gentlemen's restroom in the lobby, which was not busy. A pleasant Black man tended to the white hand towels and brushed invisible specks from his clients' jackets. He would even shine shoes upon request. All these services were performed expecting the client to leave a tip in the bowl on the counter.

Walter, once through the door, turned abruptly to confront me. "What is your problem? What are you giggling about?"

It was then that the attendant stepped forward and said, "Excuse me sir, but you have something pinned to the back collar of your jacket. It appears to have something written on it. May I remove it for you?"

Additional safety-pinned pieces of paper were retrieved from Walter's attire as the two of us stood in the tiny toilet compartment. He took off items of clothing, and I removed each numbered tag.

After receiving a whisk-broom dusting of both our jackets and a heartfelt wish that we enjoy ourselves at the Mark Hopkins Hotel, Walter gave a generous tip to the attendant.

"I swear, Raub, one more word, and I'll leave you here and go on without you."

Walter, composed after his slight embarrassment, stepped from the elevator onto the 19th floor of the Mark Hopkins Hotel and into the Vista Bar. "God, do I need a cocktail." Walter whispered.

"Why are you whispering?" I asked.

"This is a serenity bar, and conversation is discouraged. You are to enjoy your cocktail, take in the magnificent view and listen to the harp music. Any talking must be in a whisper."

Now, I knew I had heard everything from Walter Healy.

It was close to five o'clock and pitch black outside the huge glass windows. Raindrops ran down the dark tinted glass. Distant lights could be seen in the gloom. Small candles cast flickering images onto the tablecloths, which were also black. The brightest light in the room was from the music stand of the female harp player, who knew exactly where to position her fingers in the pitch-dark room.

A waitress dressed in a black uniform—she resembled a ninja fighter—bowed and directed us to our chairs, which were also black, low to the floor, and incredibly soft and squishy. The chairs were enormous wingbacks that gave the impression of sitting upright in one's own casket. She took our order and left.

An adjacent table was suddenly illuminated by the flash of a cigarette lighter, casting a light on the face of the smoker—a man as old as Methuselah. He was sitting with his wife, a woman of the same age. She had not felt the sun's warmth or had any exposure to light in at least four decades. Her chalk-white sagging skin was marked with deep wrinkles. There were crow's feet around her eyes and crimson blood-red lips. A heavily jeweled tiara jutted upward from her mass of twisted graying hair. The flickering glow of his cigarette lighter caught each of the precious stones in her tiara. It reflected colors around the room's walls. For a second, I could see the shapes of other people in this quiet black room.

Our two martinis were served. We enjoyed our own cigarettes. Two martinis later, Walter whispered that we should be leaving to get a good table at Juanita's.

How the waitress knew that we were about to leave was beyond me, but she presented me with the check. So I decided to be generous and treat Walter.

The Moroccan black leather case that held our drink tab was large, as was everything at the Mark Hopkins Hotel. For some strange reason, the amount at the bottom of the bill was only legible with a magnifying glass. Once more, with the aid of my cigarette lighter, I read the amount I was expected to pay for the four martinis. It was $28, an excessive amount when even call liquor in Seattle during the 1960s was only $2 per drink.

I paid the check and left a $4.50 tip, informing Walter it was his treat for the taxicab ride to this "Juanita's," whatever and wherever that was.

"Well, Raub, at least you can now say you were at the Top of the Mark at One Knob Hill."

The same young bellhop remembered us and produced Walter's coat and umbrella. The doorman whistled for a taxicab. I ducked quickly into the back seat and noticed that Walter had also slipped a sizeable tip to the doorman.

"The seats look clean enough, Walter," I ventured.

"Oh, I knew they would be. Only presentable drivers and taxicabs are allowed to work out of the Mark Hopkins."

Well, la-de-dah, I thought to myself as we sped away.

Chapter Three
Juanita's

The taxicab whizzed around corners, passing splendid buildings I would have loved to have spent some time in, even if it was only their lobbies, but we were headed to Juanita's Gallery, or "Ark," as she sometimes called it.

Juanita's was located at Gate 6 in Sausalito, a sleepy little community northwest of San Francisco. Our cab driver weaved through the city to the Presidio and Highway 101, proceeding northward.

"Well, what do you think of it?" Walter asked.

"Think of what?" I replied.

"The Golden Gate Bridge, dumb ass! That's what! We just crossed over the most famous bridge in the world."

"Well, how in the hell would I know? It's dark as pitch, it's raining, I'm cold and freezing, and you expect me to know it's the goddamn Golden Gate Bridge? It ain't even a gold color. Gees!"

"Oh, I'll point it out to you on our return trip. Stop bitching. Here, we're at Juanita's. Pay the driver." With that, Walter was out of the cab and opening his umbrella. His silhouette was like *Mary Poppins* as he strolled to the restaurant's entrance with his umbrella raised high in the air.

Juanita's was one of the strangest restaurants I've ever visited. It was onboard the Charles Van Damme, a decommissioned paddlewheel ferryboat. At one time, it carried cars from Marin to Richmond and later plied the waters between Martinez and Benicia. Unfortunately, the ship was old, in bad shape, and eventually sold.

In the 1950s, the Charles Van Damme no longer transported automobiles around the San Francisco Bay but was now moored at Jack London Square and serving food to diners.

For various reasons, the restaurant didn't fare too well. In the 1950s, the Charles Van Damme was sold at auction to Donion Arques. They hired tugboats to push this once gallant lady across the San Francisco Harbor to her final resting place at Gate 6 in Sausalito. Here she rode the waves of the incoming and outgoing tides month after month, lodged in the mire of the muddy Sausalito waterfront. Depending on the tide, the Charles Van Damme sat squarely in the water, but often at low tide, the ship was mired in gooey mud and listed to either port or starboard. The solution to this "lopsided" dining experience at a sloping table was to place wood blocks under the table legs. The food and drinks were served on oversized plates and glasses with high rims to reduce spillage.

Juanita Musson, extravagant *restaurateur* and *bon vivant*, was the proprietress. She catered to influential moneyed customers from all over the world. Sally Stanford, a bordello madam and restaurateur considered Juanita's Gallery her second home when not holding court in her own fashionable and expensive restaurant, Valhalla. Hollywood visitors were interviewed by columnist Herb Caen while seated at the bar on any night of the week.

Juanita was strange, unpredictable, demanding, outrageous, and contentious. She was also conciliatory, kind-hearted, and downright mean. She was Juanita, the crowds flocked to her establishment to see her, her animals, and her collection of customers who were dining.

Juanita's collection of exotic birds included cockatiels, South American parrots, macaws, parakeets (in and out of cages), and her prized possession, posing on her shoulder like a giant orchid corsage, a chattering lory bird.

Juanita wore loose-fitting muumuu dresses that were so popular in Hawaii. Her breasts were exceptionally large, extending out in front of her like a giant automobile bumper, undoubtedly supported by a firm foundation. Her breasts were a pathway for her bird—"Chattering Lory," as she called it—to travel from one of her shoulders to the other. Lory also nibbled Juanita's ear lobes, jewelry, and braided hair.

Juanita smoked, drank, ate, and probably slept with this jabbering bird affixed to her shoulder. The bird was never silent, except when it was staring you down or flapping its green and yellow wings to fly from its roosting place on her shoulder to yours. Experienced guests knew that offering one's shoulder toward the bird was an invitation for the bird to transfer to your dinner or suit jacket. An occasional deposit of the bird's excrement occurred, which Juanita passed off simply as, "Here, let me get that for you."

Caged birds were everywhere. Frisky yellow parakeets climbed over liquor bottles behind the bar, their tiny claws gripping the rim of a martini glass. On the forward bow of the ship, a Rhode Island Red chicken had a view of the entire bay from her nest as she supplied daily fresh eggs to Juanita's kitchen. There were also dogs and cats. Somehow, all the animals got along and knew to stay away from the busy waiters and cocktail servers.

Juanita's menu was not extensive but wholesome with large portions. She enjoyed serving her corn on the cob to wealthy patrons who would never serve it in their own homes. Juanita's bartenders were highly thought of in San Francisco for their over-pour, non-collection of monies, and patron gossip. Many a male patron was at a loss when a pretty girl, a total stranger, sat next to him at the bar and "thanked" him for a cocktail he had not bought for her. With an eye toward coupling, the ever-romantic bartender had supplied the libation to the man on his own. It was his way of introducing people to each other. "I just thought that it was time you two met each other."

In these early years of the sexual explosion and the hippie generation, Juanita's was a "50-50" bar. No ethnic, wealthy, poor, straight, or gay group of people attended the establishment more than any other group. It was fashionable just to be seen at Juanita's.

It was a Friday evening, and Juanita held court at the entrance to a large and packed house. She had definite rules of "first impression," as to who would be a good customer. There were two lines of customers waiting to be admitted. The line on the right had no idea that they would be standing there as long as Juanita wanted them to stand there and possibly not be admitted. They were cataloged in her mind and forever assigned to the "not acceptable" line for being either: poor looking, underdressed, overdressed, possible trouble, drunk, thought to be a vice-squad officer, or worst of all, the dreaded inspector from the Health Department. The "fashionable line" was composed of elegantly groomed young women, preferably in furs and evening gowns. Their escorts are in either tuxedo or fashionable suit attire. Also, single older men who appeared rich and horny. And anyone who seemed to be genuine and claimed to know Sally Stanford or Juanita herself.

Juanita sometimes made mistakes while seating her customers. If they ordered the cheapest item on the menu, were not ordering drinks, or were eating too slowly, they were "taking up space." One of her muscular male employees suggested to a startled customer that they should, "Eat up. I need your table."

Juanita's Gallery was rundown. No effort had been made to cover the foul odors of the Sausalito Bay waters or that it was falling apart and sinking into the murky mud.

Walter stepped forward to Juanita's lectern. She dropped her square chin to rest on her breastbone, which enabled her to look over her Woolworth bifocal glasses.

"Hello, Juanita. How are you, my dear?"

"Walter Healy, you little shit. Where ya' been? I still get people coming in here asking if I know where you're livin' and they're not bill collectors either, if you know what I mean. Come on in, honey, you can sit at the bar like ya' used to. Is this your current friend, or are ya' still lookin' for Mr. Right?"

Juanita cupped her hand under Walter's smooth, firm chin, and he kissed her hand as we walked past the dozens of others waiting for a table.

"Come along, Walter's friend. You're welcome anytime."

Juanita adjusted the lory on her shoulder as Walter extended his hand to accept the bird.

"Careful, honey. He hasn't pooped in 'bout an hour."

Juanita ordered two young gentlemen to move their barstools closer, directed her muscular employee to bring two more stools from the back, and dictated Walter's favorite drink order to the attentive bartender. "As I remember, it's a Bombay gin, straight up in a martini glass, no ice, and a twist of lemon on only one side of the rim of the glass. No vermouth. And you, honey, the same?" she asked of me.

Juanita put her thick arm around Walter's waist, planted a lipstick kiss on his cheek, and took her bird back from Walter's hand.

"Friggin' lory pooped on my shoe," said Walter after she had left.

Walter pulled a handful of stacked, twisted napkins from a pile on the bar counter, lifted his soiled shoe almost to my lap, and said, "Here. Wipe it off."

One of the young men who earlier had been asked to move his stool muttered "faggot" to Walter, which the bartender overheard. Within seconds, the two had paid their briskly presented bill. They were escorted out of Juanita's by the same muscular employee who had produced the two extra bar stools.

"Thanks," offered Walter.

"If they don't like gays, why'd they come to San Francisco?" the bartender asked.

An array of appetizers arrived, courtesy of Juanita. The friendly bartender helped himself to a large pink cooked shrimp and offered a sprig of parsley to a pair of yellow and green parakeets, who had built a nest in the stacked glasses at the end of the bar.

"Look out for the blue macaw," a deep voice said from behind us.

Walter turned to the older man standing behind my stool. The man was dressed in the 1940s high fashion of English tweeds. He wasn't overweight, just paunchy around the waist and his patterned dress shirt was obviously a wash-and-wear. He wore an ascot around his neck and was losing his hair—long wisps were brushed forward to hide the fact.

"I'm sorry, but you look familiar. Have we met before?" asked Walter as he rose from his barstool to amplify his 6-foot-tall sartorial splendor.

"Don't be an ass and sit down. We have never met, but I am about to meet this delightful example of common Americana sitting next to you. I write about such people as you in my books. My name is Roger Danbury. I am a very successful author. Have you read any of my books? Of course, you haven't, but we will correct that. Now, I must be truthful. I know exactly who you are and where you are heading. You are Walter Healy, in all your pretentious *habiliments* and pomposity. And you, my dear boy, are Robert Karr, or better known to your close friends, of which you have hundreds more than Walter, as 'Raub.' You are both from Seattle, where you, Walter, live a *mundane* existence in the world of women's fashion, and you, Raub, my dear sweet boy, have taken on a project of the restoration of an ancient building, chipping the surface of one red brick at a time, all because of your love of architecture and reconstruction. I, Roger Danbury, know all about the two of you."

"And exactly who is Roger Danbury, and what books have you written other than cookbooks or school manuals?" a now vicious Walter inquired.

"Sensing your affinity for comic books and the humor of the funnies in your newspapers, have you ever read or even heard of a book entitled, *Auntie Mame,* or *Guestward, Ho!*? Under the name of Patrick Dennis. I am the only author to ever have had three books on the *New York Times* Bestseller List at the same *time*. That's who I am."

Impressed by this loud, outspoken man, Walter suddenly became enchanted with the new acquaintance and offered him a libation. He promptly accepted as he pulled a vacant barstool into the space between us.

"Now, gentlemen, I have some other news for you. We are all three onboard the SS Caprice, headed to enchantingly mysterious Mexico. Unfortunately, it is not the intellectual cities we will be visiting, such as the ancient lands of the Aztec: Cozumel, Veracruz, Colima, or even Mexico City itself, but we shall find some divertissement for our interests along the way. I had noticed the two of you on the first night aboard ship, and then when you switched tables to join that frightfully filthy-rich woman, Mrs. Winton, and her repugnant grandson. A few discreet questions to shipboard personnel provided your names and background. Forgive me, but exactly what time is it that we are supposed to be on board before departing for Los Angeles, the 'City of the Angels' as it is called?"

"Sailing time is midnight or before the first bell of the middle watch, as Walter would say, but I think he has had one too many Bombay martinis to offer his expert seamanship knowledge." I said, then added. "Since Walter is now passed out with his head on the counter, shall we finish our libations and call a taxicab?"

Walter had a great tolerance for alcohol, as did our new shipmate, Roger Danbury. However, for some reason, probably his being back in his hometown and seeing Juanita again, Walter had slowly slipped away.

Roger gathered his nearly full cocktail and proceeded to the piano bar. It was break time for the trio, and Roger slid across the piano bench like a pro about to perform a Scriabin Prelude or a Bach Etude. But, instead, he struck only one note on the black keys, an e-flat. Then he swished a gulp of his cocktail. Magically, a hush fell on the entire room as he began to sing Cole Porter's "I Concentrate on You."

"Whenever skies look gray to me. And trouble begins to brew. Whenever the winter winds become too strong, I concentrate on you."

At this point, the trio, finishing their break, returned to their instruments. Roger slid off the piano bench. He continued singing. "When fortune cries, 'Nay, nay' to me … "

The trio joined in, and the volume intensified for the song's finale.

Juanita and the entire house broke into resounding applause with demands of "Encore," "More," and shouts of "Who was that?"

Roger Danbury assisted me in carrying Walter to a waiting taxicab. The entire evening had been "comped" by Juanita after Roger sheepishly divulged the startling truth that he had but $4 in his wallet.

I gladly paid the taxicab fare upon arriving at the SS Caprice, where two longshoremen grabbed Walter by his extended arms and carried him up the gangplank. Two able seamen took him from there to our cabin, where he was dumped unceremoniously on his bed.

The SS Caprice set sail at midnight for Los Angeles. At the same time, Roger Danbury and I explored the offerings of an onboard pizza parlor. Other than Juanita's complimentary *hors d'oeuvres,* none of us had eaten since lunch. Roger and I shared a giant "extravaganza" and discussed the evening's activities.

"What's this business about you only having $4 in your pocket? Did you forget to bring more money with you when you went out tonight?"

"Actually Raub, my dear boy, that is the extent of the Patrick Dennis fortune at the moment. Not only is this the pitiful amount of my wealth for at least another month or so until I can wiggle another advance out of my publisher, but I have written a check to a poor, old, confused man for the boat ticket on this voyage to Mexico. Unfortunately, the checking account I wrote the check on has insufficient funds. I trust that my poor wife will have the sense to cover the insufficient amount. She's also a writer, published too; lots of keen Vassar College stuff, a woman's angle, and decorating your home. How she puts up with me, I'll never know. My life has been in such a terrible confusion the past few years, I hardly remember what my two children even look like... hopefully, they look like their mother. You wouldn't happen to have a fiver sitting around someplace? I could pay you back once I hit up my publisher."

I withdrew my wallet from my jacket, thumbed through the cash, and handed him a $5 bill.

"Oh, dear boy, I meant five thousand, although I will keep this for at least some type of a tip to my cabin boy before I jump ship."

His words about jumping ship made me think he would jump overboard and commit suicide. I was horrified.

Roger read my thoughts. "No, no dear boy, I am way too vainglorious to take my own life. I have thousands and thousands of notes and ideas for future books, a play about a prostitute, and even a musical that I want Marlene Dietrich to star in. Oh, don't worry. Something will turn up before I disappear in the jungles of rural Mexico. I am famished for the indigenous native life. Do you think I'll have trouble finding proper writing paper? Maybe I should just concentrate on writing story lines on yellow pads and do the fine writing back in New York City. My dear boy, I am so energized tonight. I am, what do you say, 'all geared up.' I feel I could write an entire book tonight. Come to my cabin, such as it is. I think I still have a pour or two in one of my bottles I managed to bring with me from the abode of Roger Danbury."

Roger's cabin was far grander than what Walter and I were sharing. He not only had an easily accessible bathroom but two closets, a full writing desk with a portable typewriter, a leather sofa, and two companion side chairs.

"Roger, what did this set you back? And why would you write a worthless check for such a large cabin?" I asked.

"I didn't make the selection of this cabin. It was made by the man I wrote the check to. You see, dear boy, what I told you at Juanita's is correct. My name is Patrick Dennis, at least that is the name I use for most of my writing. My actual birth name is Edward Everett Tanner III. I'm an Illinois boy. Roger Danbury is the poor old man who bought this ticket for a cruise to Mexico, but is currently suffering from a serious ailment: gout, I believe he said, or was it grand palsy? Anyway, he had paid for the cabin before he discovered he was unable to travel, and I offered him a fair price to take the ticket off his hands, but for some silly, stupid reason, I must use the name while on board."

"But Roger, Patrick Dennis, whatever you want to be called. What are you going to do when the real Roger Danbury sends your worthless check off to his bank to be deposited and comes back as NSF? He will probably call the police and charge you with theft of the ticket and order that you be arrested. I have never had the pleasure of spending time in a Mexican prison, but I can assure you those that have, never wanted to repeat the same mistake twice."

"I am sure the honorable Roger Danbury and the rest of his law firm will not want to press charges against me. I was his houseguest in Seattle for several weeks, and he seemed such a kindly sort. Very *de rigueur,* I would say. Old Seattle money, you know."

"I thought the name of Danbury sounded familiar. The Danbury you have given a worthless check to is the Honorable Roger 'sue-em' Danbury? He owns half of downtown Seattle. He's not known for his generosity, other than an occasional vocal 'thank you' to a judge who has ruled in his favor."

"I found him most entertaining. We were working on a plan for me to write his memoirs. I have some of his notes here someplace."

"Mr. Dennis, I mean Patrick, you have a problem far more reaching than the worthless check to Roger Danbury. You are entering a foreign country illegally. Mexico, to be exact. Do you, at least, have an American passport to prove who you are?"

"Of course, dear boy, I have a passport. I've been all over the world with it. Did you know that I served the United States military in South Africa, and I've been all through Europe... first class, you can be sure!"

"And is the name Patrick Dennis on this passport, or are you using the name of Dame Daphne du Maurier this season?"

"*Au contraire, mon ami!* Let me show you. It reads Edward Everett Tanner III. Patrick Dennis is my writing name. I told you that."

Roger Danbury, Patrick Dennis, née Edward Everett Tanner III was getting testy. He shoved his passport into my face.

"See, that is my picture. I am an American citizen, and I have rights like anyone else!"

"Actually, Patrick, if I may call you that. You have no rights in Mexico with or without this passport. Showing or offering a different name than what you are using at this moment is a criminal offense. Even if you jump ship in Los Angeles or fall overboard as we pass San Diego, you will be caught by Roger Danbury, Attorney at Law, gout or no gout. He always gets his man. You obviously bragged to him about your books. It will be rather easy for him to track down your legal name and add it to the warrant for your arrest and extradition from Mexico."

Patrick swallowed the last of his cheap vodka in one gulp.

"I guess maybe three or four years in prison, at the most. Work a deal where you can take your typewriter with you," I added.

"Can't," said Patrick. "It belongs to Mr. Danbury."

Chapter Four

Getting to Know Our Fellow Shipmates

The following day, neither Walter nor I saw even a gleam of light reflecting from the balding head of Patrick Dennis, traveling incognito as the illustrious Seattle attorney, Roger Danbury.

I told Walter of my late-night conversation with Patrick and the dilemma he was facing with only $9 to his name, or rather the name of Roger Danbury. I was sure he would be whisked away at any moment to either a United States or Mexican prison and never be heard from again.

The telephone in our tiny cabin rang at 4:30 that afternoon. I answered it. It was Edith Winton, requesting our company for a small cocktail party in her cabin suite. "I just met the most fascinating man, who claims to be a personal friend of the two of you. He is Patrick Dennis, the famous author. I can only accommodate about thirty people in my little suite, but I want you two to come early. Patrick is coming at 5:30, so you come when he does. I've arranged with the captain to have Patrick at our table from now on. I knew you wouldn't mind. Poor dear had some terrible mix-up about some name he is traveling under. I never did understand all this business about writers and their non du plumb. I just told him I was gonna' call him just plain old Patrick Dennis, but I still don't understand who this Tanner fellow is. So I called the shipping line and told them to send the fare money to this nasty attorney, a Mr.

Danbury, and that I was covering all of Patrick's expenses until we get to Acapulco, where he said he would contact his publishers for the money and pay me back for the liner tickets."

"Actually, Edith, Patrick Dennis is his pen name, his *nom de plume,* it is called. It's his pseudonym. His birth name is Edward Everett Tanner III."

"Funny, when I called the shipping office, they couldn't find any record of ever booking Patrick or ever receiving any money under either of his names, only this Roger Danbury fellow. Well, never mind. It's all straightened out now, and I'm having a ton of Patrick's books flown down to Puerto Vallarta. Oh, I'm so excited! A real author, and he's so funny, too." Edith giggled. "He sure is educated and well-traveled. Why, he's been all over the world. I asked him how he ever got all the way up to Seattle, and he said he had flown non-stop from Tokyo to Seattle after leaving Tunis. Don't rightly know where that is, but he said he had lived in Cairo, Paris, and Madrid as well. He also said somethin' about writing a biography for some fellow up in Seattle, but it didn't pan out. Did Patrick ever say to you two how he happened to lose all of his money, and why he's usin' Mr. Danbury's cruise tickets?"

"I think it all happened when he started working for this attorney fellow, who from past experience and notoriety in the Seattle papers, is known to be quite a shyster himself. Not that I'm implying that Mr. Dennis has done anything wrong. I'm sure it's simply a case of a giant mix-up. Walter and I will be most happy to join you and your other guests, in their meeting Patrick. The past days of being with him have been most interesting. Tomorrow, we dock at Mazatlan. Walter tells me that you have arranged for an afternoon of deep-sea fishing for David, and that Captain Cartwright has set up the entire boat rental and crew to attend to the two of you for the afternoon. That should be fun. Has David ever been deep-sea fishing before?"

"I'm afraid not. My husband, before he passed away, made several jaunts out of San Diego Harbor, but only for the day," Edith admitted. "I was always so sick. Just getting on board with the ups and downs of the boat, I would have to go below deck and lie down. We should be fine tomorrow. The ship's onboard doctor has fixed us up with scopolamine patches. David and I both have them stuck behind our ear. We'll see how it goes. Would you and Walter care to come along? I can arrange it. Patrick has refused my invitation. He said he had to stay onboard, something about receiving a message from his publisher. He is such a nice man. He offered to prepare our catch for tomorrow night's dinner. He claims to be a highly sought-after *gourmand*."

Yes, "sought after" is an adequate description of Patrick Dennis, I thought to myself. Wait until the Mexican immigration authorities catch up with him after he jumps ship.

"I had asked Dennis to come in formal wear tonight, but he claims that some negligent room attendant burnt a hole in his tuxedo, and he is now reduced to wearing either his gray or dark brown suit. You realize that the entire crew is Italian or something, don't you? I do know that very few of them speak English, and some of the others look and act like escaped criminals. That's why I always bring a small staff from my house on these trips. I'd just die if my maid, Gloria, burnt a hole in one of my gowns. My husband firmly believed in giving the less fortunate countries of Europe the opportunity to 'lift themselves up by the bootstraps' he used to say."

"I wouldn't call Italy one of the 'less fortunate countries of Europe.' I can name at least five other 'unfortunate' countries who are equally as poor and unable to provide employment for its people. The contracts your husband signed with unscrupulous labor federations of these countries borders on modern-day slavery."

Mrs. Winton reacted in shock that her husband, with his hundreds of European crew members working on one of his ocean liners, merited the accusation of slavery. "I'll have you know, Mr. Karr, that my husband cared for his workers. Yes, many of them could not speak English, but were quick to learn what their jobs were all about. Oh, they didn't make the usual $5 an hour the Americans were being paid, but when they shared their tips, they did all right. Most of them sent money back to their needy families in their home countries."

"That's all well and good, Mrs. Winton, but I know for a fact that until three years ago, under your husband's direction, these same underpaid, overworked, and totally ignorant-of-their-rights employees were being paid in 'Lots.' I am not saying they were being fed an extraordinary amount of food, because they weren't. 'Lots' is the acronym for 'Left over table scraps.' These poor workers were being fed plate scrapings from the dining room: food that had been partially eaten by the passengers on the liner, leftovers from the kitchen, as well as that food which the cooks designated as either partially rotten or soon to spoil. Where have you been for the past few years, Mrs. Winton? Were you not aware of the terrible accusations and charges filed against your husband?"

"I know nothing of this cruise business. My husband, bless his soul, died two years ago, and I had to step in and take over running his company. The food issue was corrected immediately when my cabin valet told me how terrible the crew's food was. I, personally, have supervised the cooking in the kitchens for months, and along with a newly appointed head chef, I ended the policy of serving the help terrible food. Those responsible: the chefs, first mates, pursers, and the captains at that time were relieved of their positions immediately. I watched as I made sure those responsible for this terrible act were served the food they had planned for the entire crew during the balance of the trip. All my employees now eat a well balanced diet, and I make surprise inspections of the kitchen on every voyage. And, Mr. Karr, as for my employees not speaking or understanding English, do you know that we have volunteer English classes each evening and that those employees who partake in the classes are paid for attending? I have prevailed upon darling Patrick to tour the kitchens with me. He seems so knowledgeable about food items and presentation at the tables, which is so important; don't you think? What hasn't he done?" asked Mrs. Winton.

"Yes, what hasn't Mr. Dennis done?" I replied with a tone of smugness in my voice.

Walter and I left her to plan her cocktail party.

We didn't believe Edith's retelling of Patrick's plight of a tuxedo misfortune. Still, we did choose to wear similar, non-formal clothing so that Patrick wouldn't "stand out" at the party.

Walter was flawlessly dressed in his best black business suit, while I wore gray slacks and my trusty navy-blue jacket. It was 4:45 pm when a rhythmic knock sounded on our cabin door.

"Tah, tah-tah, tah, tah... tah, tah."

Contrary to Patrick's claims of having his evening's formalwear burnt to a crisp by his vacuous Italian cabin boy, he stood before us blazingly sharp-looking in a handsome wide lapel formal tuxedo.

"My dear boys, you are aware that Edith said that tonight's dress is formal, aren't you?"

"I'm only wearing my black suit to be more harmonious with what I thought you would be wearing tonight. You don't think for one minute that we believed that story about Guido Salmaggi leaving his steam iron on your Tony Martin tuxedo, do you? I told Raub you would probably show up in the English tweed outfit you wore when we met at Juanita's," Walter retorted with a smirk.

"Fortunately, I have a way with people of all classes and always have been able to gain assistance no matter the problem is by being my charming, loveable self, Walter. You are quite correct in your assumption that my limited amount of *garmenture* does not contain a formal tuxedo or even a tenth of the dress business suits you seem to have in your possession. Still, a subtle word to my cabin manservant provided no less than five formal dinner wears to choose from. There are fourteen dinner waiters aboard this ship, and most own two tuxedo working outfits. It was rather disheartening that the finer imported tuxedos presented to me were unfortunately owned by the shorter, more rotund waiters. It seems that wealth relates to stomach girth proportionately. If you haven't noticed, I am slightly taller than you are, being 6' 2," to be exact. I am best fitted in size 42-long, which whittles down the garments that were offered to me considerably."

"What are those strips of the shiny lapel fabric on the cusp of each sleeve?" I asked nervously.

"Well, my dear boy, I am blessed with long, athletic swimmers' arms. The one tuxedo offered with trousers that fit my waist and were long enough for my masculine legs was owned by a swarthy wine steward whose arms are shorter than mine. The ship's seamstress painstakingly let out the excess material from the end of each sleeve. Then she fashioned the strips from a lesser tuxedo lapel, which was donated for the cause. Through her meticulous hand sewing, she was able to cover the off-color wear marks of the previous wearer." Patrick proudly flashed his arms for us to see. "I think it might set a new trend in haberdashery. Don't you think? It gives a 'naval' quality, like the ship captain's jacket with his stripes showing his rank."

"Well, Vice-Admiral Dennis, since you are in tuxedo wear, I shall change accordingly," Walter said eagerly. "I wouldn't want you to stand out as the only tuxedo wearer during dinner tonight. Robert will have to crouch in a corner and hope that he doesn't draw too much attention with his junior-college wear."

"Oh, I have taken the liberty of bringing my cabin man and two offerings of proper apparel for Raub. I peg you as a size 39-long. I don't think any of these black trousers are long enough for you, my dear boy. Try this white tuxedo jacket on for size. I don't think it will raise too many eyebrows amongst our fellow passengers, being that most of them will be wearing bib-overalls and work boots. On second thoughts, this is a bad idea, Raub. The white dinner jacket looks fine, but not with your gray trousers. Besides, it is well past Labor Day to be wearing white anyway."

In their black tuxedos and I, feeling more comfortable in my post-college attire, the two boulevardiers arrived at Edith's suite promptly at 5:30 pm, all eager and bursting for a cocktail.

As we entered the partially filled stateroom, I was amused that Patrick knew everyone and enjoyed offering introductions to Mrs. Winton and even Captain Cartwright.

Dennis joked, told stories, sang, and read from his latest novel during the next hour and a half. He also charmed the 'bejesus' out of every lady present with his story of meeting Marlene Dietrich in London. This was followed by a flawless interpretation of her "Falling in Love Again" routine.

A cabin attendant rang the dinner gong, and the cocktail party, a glittering success, ended. Patrick rushed to Edith Winton's side. He physically pushed young David into Walter's lap, and issued instructions to Walter and me that the boy was not joining us for dinner in the dining room. "Do call room service and provide the boy with whatever he desires for his evening meal: a hot dog, caviar, hamburgers, anything his tormented little heart desires. Put the charges on your ship's account, and I shall reimburse you at the next port of call."

Walter subdued the wiggling David with a tight grip about the neck. "Most certainly, sahib. I shall also add a most gracious sum of money as a gratuity to the bill. Do order your dinner cocktails without us. We shall be down shortly. Come on, David. Let's get your food ordered, and then I'm having your room steward lock you in your bedroom. You're not running the entire ship tonight, so behave yourself. I don't want to miss one word of Roger Danbury, Edward Everett Tanner III, or Patrick Dennis tonight."

Chapter Five
A Day in Mazatlan

The *bahia* into Mazatlan was a flurry of small boats, each equipped with the tall bamboo spring poles that trailed the baited hooks in the water far beyond the wake of the fast-traveling motorboats.

Edith asked that Walter and I come to the docks to see young David and her off for their day of deep-sea fishing.

"I just don't know what I'll do if little David catches a marlin. It's such a big fish. I've seen them all stuffed or mounted or whatever they do to them on the Seattle Yacht Club walls. Terrible sight they are. Oh, I know they're just plaster and paint, but they shouldn't be there in the first place. I think I'll just faint or something if he catches even one fish. David, don't touch anything when we get onboard. Do you hear? Walter, Raub, please reconsider and come with us. I need someone to manage David if I get seasick and have to lay down."

"I'm sorry, Edith, but both of us can barely stand the gentle rocking of the SS Caprice. You know how you have to walk down the center of the hallways aboard ship? Well, Walter can't walk on deck, and at the same time look out at the waves without wanting to throw up," I answered.

The captain was eager to get started and revved the engines. The pungent smell of ignited gasoline from the engines engulfed us as two young Mexican boys extended their arms to help Edith aboard. In a flash, they were leaving the pier, lurching into open waters and out to sea.

Edith gave a faint goodbye wave as if she were being exiled to a remote island by a ruthless emperor. David was swinging his legs as he spun around and around on the stool at the boat's aft, ready to begin his first deep-sea fishing experience.

"What time do the bars open in this sardine can?" Walter asked.

After a short walk from the docks, we found ourselves in the middle of the market or *mercado*—a collection of open-door restaurants, bars, and one shop that seemed to be run as a day school for a bunch of screaming children. The teacher, or the person in charge, had no control over these children. All were poorly dressed, and several little girls were without underpants under their tube-like homemade dresses.

"Good God!" Walter shouted. "The oldest girl must be only seven or eight. Raub, it must be 120 degrees in the shade. Get me out of this hell hole before I throw up. Now I wish I had gone with Edith on the boat."

"Walter, we are in the poorest section of the city. One doesn't have to be a mentalist to realize we could get into a lot of trouble in this part of town. Don't dally, walk in a straight line away from the harbor. We'll head for that tall building over there. It must be a hotel or something."

As we approached the doorway, I stopped Walter. "No, Walter, that's the police station, and I don't think either of us want to go in there. Just keep walking and try to stop looking so much like a stupid, hung-over American tourist."

We headed for an open-air café.

"Let's sit down and have coffee, at least to get our bearings and figure out the best way to get back to the ship."

"I told you I want a drink!" Walter shouted.

"Cool it. You're becoming 'the ugly American,' and people are starting to stare. Here's a vacant table away from the sidewalk. I'll see if they have a drink for you or at least a beer. Sit down."

Walter stood and adjusted the salt, sugar, and varieties of hot sauces on the bare plastic-topped table. Eventually, he sat down.

"This table is filthy!" he shouted in a loud voice. "Look, the flies are having a banquet on the silverware. There should be a law. And who are you to be calling me 'ugly?'"

No more than thirteen years of age, a young Mexican girl strolled up to Walter and took his hand. Walter reacted immediately as if he had been bitten by an Egyptian viper. "Get this teenage Cleopatra off me!" Walter yelled, knocking the table over.

"Do lower your voice, Walter," ordered Patrick, who had been observing all the commotion for some time. "You're exhibiting all the things people from all over the world despise about America. *Uno Cerveza, por favor,*" he asked a waitress.

"How did you get down to the docks? I thought you were staying onboard today, to get some writing done, for a change."

"To be honest, Raub, I was planning to jump ship here in Mazatlan and begin my wandering, away from the major tourist traps further south, but after seeing the poverty and living conditions, I have reconsidered and will return to the ship with you." Patrick was getting huffy. "Finish your beer, Walter, and come along. You may carry my typewriter and bag of writing supplies. Raub, be a good boy and pay the waitress for the beer, would you? I seem to have spent the fiver you gave me the other night on taxi fare to get down here. The driver said the fare was $10 peso. I gave him the $5 bill. Did I over tip him? Come along, Walter. I'll buy you a real cocktail onboard. At least, I still have credit there." Patrick was anxious to leave. "Oh, move it, Walter. Bring the last of your damn beer with you. I missed breakfast this morning, and here you are, guzzling down beer at ten o'clock in the morning."

I paid for the taxicab back to the SS Caprice, paying the driver exactly one 10 peso coin, plus another $10-peso as a tip. A total of about $2.50."

"Dennis, if you're going to be on your own here in Mexico, we must have a few lessons on how to not get screwed out of what little money you have, or rather, the money that was once *mine*."

"Speaking of money, what am I supposed to do with all of these odd-shaped coins? They weigh a ton in my pockets, and I have no idea what they are worth, but I see people using them constantly."

Two fistfuls of Mexican coins cascaded across the desk in Patrick's cabin and rolled on the floor.

"Patrick, you have about $500 pesos in coins. That's about $40 US dollars. You're rich," offered Walter, who was aching for another beer.

"You weren't really going to jump ship here in Mazatlan, were you?" I asked.

"I was, until I experienced firsthand the absolute poverty and dismal living conditions of these poor people. It is a village frequented by American fishermen, bent on pulling behemoth-finned creatures from the ocean, only to hang them upside down here on the docks, weigh them, and then have their pictures taken with the carcass. Eventually it will be shipped off to some taxidermy concern in East Overshoe, Wisconsin, where it will be cast in plaster, wire, and shiny paint, and there it will remain for the next fifty years screwed to the wall of Joe Blow's office at the Poppin' Fun Popcorn factory. No, Raub, I changed my mind about beginning my sojourn into the alien world of *Española Mexico* after reaching the second step of the gangplank of the SS Caprice and smelling the putrid, foul smell of rotting fish guts, burning beans, the fermenting *pulque* they call beer, and the slippery vomit on the dusty sidewalk. That's when. I don't relish the idea of a face-to-face confrontation with Edith over dinner tonight. She will obviously want me to confirm or deny some of my last night's statements, especially the one about Cary Grant and Randolph Scott's homosexuality. Cripes sakes, they lived together in Hollywood for over a year until the studios got wind of it and said, 'Butch it up, boys, or you're out of a job.' I did see one rather respectable-looking restaurant at the beginning of the *Malecón,* and since I have so much money on me now, I'll treat for lunch, but Walter, you have to pay for your own beers, or have you progressed to the hard stuff already?"

As the three of us rounded the corner onto the *Malecón,* we encountered a young Mexican streetwalker trying to get Walter's attention. She gripped his arm.

"Get this tramp away from me!" he shouted.

"Vamos, you little tramp! Get back to your *prosti la casa!"* Dennis yelled.

"I welcome your assistance, but your few hours of reading a Spanish/English *Diccionario* has you ill-prepared to speak to these people in their own language," related Walter. "The word is pronounced 'bamos'. V words are pronounced as B words: 'Bamos,' 'Get away,' 'Let's go.' Also, your *'prosti la casa'* should be *'prostibulo,'* a whore house."

Dennis yanked the woman's death grip from Walter's hand and thrust a handful of Mexican coins in her now-trembling hand. *"Vamos!"* he yelled at her. "None of us are interested in you, you little *punta.* Look how she struts her stuff. She thinks she's a real *mujer atractiva y excitante,* a real Mexican sexpot. None of us want to have sex with you. We demand privacy, *aislamiento.* We are going back to our *boato,* the *SS Capricho,* where we are *pasamanos* on the *océano* and will *hacerse a la mar* away from this *excrement y orina* hole. Vamos!"

An elderly woman appeared from a doorway and struck a pose as if to strike Dennis. *"Bastardo!"* she yelled, along with other unfavorable names.

"I don't know where to start, but I will give it a try," said Walter. "The word for whore or prostitute is *'puta'. 'Punta'* means the sharp end of a stick or point. *'Pasamano'* is a banister on a staircase. You meant *'pasajero,'* passenger, you idiot, and as far as your *'hacerse a la mar,'* none of us are going to change into sea water. The SS Caprice is a *'barco,'* not a 'boato.' 'Boato' means ostentatious or pompous, like you. Well, now that we have all of that settled, the locals now know for certain of your lunacy. If you are going to complete your insane plan of jumping ship in Mexico, may I suggest you use some of that Mexican money in your pocket, of which I doubt you have very much left, and buy yourself a good dictionary or a paid translator to speak your words for you? That looks like a nice café up ahead. I'm parched, and I'll treat for all our lunch and drinks. Shall we, *Muchachos?"*

Chapter Six

A Lazy Afternoon in Sleepy Mazatlan

By the time we finished lunch, Dennis and Walter were not speaking. The three of us returned in silence to the SS Caprice. In fact, none of us were speaking to each another. Dennis harbored a resentment that I didn't speak up for him at the docks. Then there was that terrible scene at the café when Dennis tossed the remainder of his Mexican coins on the luncheon table attempting to pay the tab.

The money was not wasted. A horde of giggling Mexican children appeared within seconds, snatching up rolling coins from under other diners' feet. It caused much confusion and laughter. While Walter determined how much money to leave on the $560-peso bill, approximately $39 US, I grabbed the check and shoved two twenties and a five-dollar bill into the waitress's hand. "*Tuya,*" I said in answer to her broad smile.

"Thank you," she answered in perfect English.

We were halfway back to the ship. We had decided to walk, forgoing a dilapidated taxicab. Still, the streets were busy, and Walter insisted on being a total ass in displaying his expertise in speaking Spanish to Dennis.

"*Almoner,*" he said, alerting Dennis to the old man seated in rags and no shoes on the curb. The old man was toothless.

"*Salir!*" Walter shouted, waving his arms in the air as if shooing away.

Then I realized there was a real problem between Dennis and Walter. Both stood firm, with a look of bravado in their eyes. They both stood like Clint Eastwood facing each other, pistols half drawn.

"Patrick, you walk up the path ahead of us," I suggested.

"You, *El Idiota,* Walter. You walk behind me at least ten paces and shut your mouth."

Walter sheepishly remained silent.

Patrick stepped backward and bumped into a young girl. "You have been in the sun too long, my dear. You are '*quemadura de sol*'; you are sunburned. I advise you to seek shelter and partake in a good shower to rid your skin of the multitude of infections that float in this foul Mexican air. If you don't, it will cause inflammation and will irritate your skin even further."

The young woman gripped each breast and said, "*No comprendo, Señor, Gustarie a teta?*"

"Madam, I assure you, I have no interest in your breasts, your *titi*, or any other part of your body. *Salir! Vagar!* Away from me this instant!"

I'd had enough of this. "Patrick, I suggest you get your butt over next to Walter and prepare to defend yourself. Do you realize that you just offended that woman by calling her a *titi*, a South American monkey? From the looks of that shady character she has been talking to, he must be her agent or pimp. *Alcahuete,* I think he is called."

Patrick rolled his eyes and did a sign of the cross on his chest as we saw uniformed *policia* take a seat outside the sidewalk café we were passing.

"*Buenos dias.*" Patrick called out to the girl and her pimp. "*Gozar de café.*"

The woman, disappointed but anxious to secure a more willing participant for the day, ambled off as we continued our journey back to the SS Caprice.

Once onboard, Walter went to the closest open bar alone. Patrick bid us farewell and said he was off to pound the typewriter's keys. I was at a loss as to what to do. I knew that our cabin would be hot and stuffy, and very little was going on aboard the ship as we were in port for the day.

When the captain saw me without Mrs. Winton, he became concerned about her whereabouts. He thought I had gone deep-sea fishing with her and her grandson, David. "I am sure Mrs. Winton is perfectly fine, but I thought you were helping her with her grandson, little David. I know the fishing boat captain personally and I instructed him to take extreme care in dealing with little David. I'm sure you know what I mean, Mr. Karr. Mrs. Winton sees no harm in any of little David's pranks. In any case, I shall have a taxicab standing by to speed up their return from the adventure."

"I hope the boat captain has good insurance," I warned.

"David can be a handful and isn't so 'little' when it comes to causing damage. If Mrs. Winton is incapacitated and under the weather from seasickness, there will be no one that David will listen to or obey."

There was nothing I could do to ease Captain Cartwright's concern, so I went to a bar near the entrance to the main dining room. I was in luck, as only one other couple was seated at a small table, rapt in conversation. It must be the beginning of a shipboard romance, I thought. It's a little odd. He was wearing a wedding band, but she wasn't.

Suddenly, I heard clicking sounds coming from the far end of the bar. I turned but saw no one. The clicking stopped, then started up again, only to pause, then start up again.

It was then that I noticed Patrick Dennis seated cross-legged on the carpeted floor with his typewriter between his long, gangly legs. Piles of loose papers were stacked around him. Two empty Bloody Mary glasses held open a reference book and a well-worn binder containing his "future ideas." He was deeply immersed in his work, oblivious to everything around him.

"Anybody," he snorted, "How do you spell *époque,* as in '*belle époque*,' the works of an *artiste,* you know, an '*oeuvre*', a lifetime of writing? Does anybody know?"

The bar was silent, except for the sound of a glass being washed behind the bar and Patrick's fury of clicking typewriter keys. The loving couple had now gone elsewhere to continue their romance.

"Somebody, say something!" Patrick demanded.

"Are you writing a biography of Michelangelo Buonarroti?" I asked, "Or are you puffing up your obituary, Patrick? Either one, but don't forget to include the 'im' words, like 'impolite,' 'impetuous,' 'impatient,' and certainly don't forget 'imperfect.' Your ego is as large and as cold as one of Michelangelo's sculptures. If you stop that clicking of the typewriter, I will spell *époque* for you."

"Hello, Raub. You're just in time to hear my composed speech for Mrs. Winton. She asked me to write something she could read out before she introduces me at tonight's entertainment. I thought I would read a few chapters from *Auntie Mame,* or do you think something from *Guestward Ho!* would be better?"

"Patrick, you are so full of it. I believe you could read from the Captain's engine-room logs and make it entertaining. Have you given any thought to what Walter and I will be facing once you disappear from the ship? And speaking of you jumping ship, I imagine it will be a quiet 'Where's Patrick? Since it is not to be here in Mazatlan, is it going to be the affluent, tranquil beaches of Puerto Vallarta, or will you be 'hobnobbing' with the Hollywood movie crowd in Acapulco? You really should warn us so that we can pinch our cheeks to look as though we have been crying over your disappearance when they come to question us."

"I will keep you well informed once I have set my flawless plan into motion. You make 'jumping ship' sound like I am going to do a swan dive off the bow of the SS Caprice wearing one of Veloz's dance capes."

"Furthermore, oh great literary wizard, I would be careful where you choose to use the words 'jump ship.' Bartenders have ears and empty pockets, and you have made a measly effort of tipping them for drinks and food. Walter and I tip onboard at the time of each purchase. It wouldn't surprise me if, not only the police searched all of Mexico for you, but also the waiters, bartenders, and stewards, from this ship."

"Raub, you know of my financial situation, and I don't think that over-tipping is a favorable gesture in teaching these backward and mostly illiterate people the value of a dollar."

"Oh, Patrick, you have such a way with the words. The poor over-worked waiter sees you as the rich American tourist who has spent thousands of Mexican pesos to get on this tub. If you were in his place, wouldn't you wonder why, after enjoying a $50-dinner, you have only left a tip of a few pennies on the table? It has been fun meeting and getting to know you, Patrick, but leave us out of your plans, especially Walter. He's very fragile. He believes he's returning to Seattle to face a major employment problem. He told me last night that it was not his idea to take this vacation to Mexico, but it was forced upon him by his employers. He suspects they are interviewing his replacement as we sit here, in this harbor of Mazatlan. He keeps asking me questions like, 'How will Patrick survive after jumping ship with no money?' and he worries about your limited and always incorrect Spanish. For your information, Walter speaks perfect Spanish. He even hinted that he might join you in your adventure."

"Did he really call it an adventure, Raub? Does he really think that this is a game with me? That I am desperate to get away from New York, my wife and children, my agent, who is an ass of gigantic proportions— he thinks that I can survive on an allowance of $40 a week. Don't get me wrong, he is excellent at his job, but I have to beg for everything I request from him. I figure that if I am incommunicado for a period of time, my agent and publisher will start looking for that next book and ease up a little. As for the wife and kids, I'm sorry, but I need my space right now, and my space is right here on this boat—or do you think I should take that swan dive from the bow of the ship?"

I left him to his typing. I had to prepare for Edith Winton and sweet little David, who were due to return from their deep-sea fishing trip.

The fishing trip had not gone well. David had caught a marlin and a large one at that. Edith was horrified by the size of it. She expected something smaller, like a king salmon or a mackerel. Something the size that she had dined on as a child in her mother's Jewish household following shul.

"David! Do stop poking at the eyes of that poor dead thing. Captain, what do we do with this hideous thing?"

"Have it mounted," suggested the captain of the fishing boat.

"But where would we put it? Not in my home!"

Edith slumped back against the banquette on the deck of the fishing boat. She covered her eyes against the harsh sunlight and tried to keep the wind from messing with her expensive hairdo as the fishing boat headed speedily toward the docks.

"Oh, Captain, do slow down. I don't care how long it takes us to get back to the SS Caprice. They'll just have to delay departure for Puerto Vallarta until I get back on board," she said.

It was late afternoon, and most of the other passengers were safely back on board and in the various cocktail bars anticipating a fun-packed evening. Sailing time was 5 p.m., and the captain was anxiously standing by for the arrival of Mrs. Winton, David, and the fish. "I want a full crew down on the docks when she arrives. Get the ship's photographer ready. Have the maintenance crew hoist a block and tackle to raise the fish up on the pier. I want photos of everybody posed with that fish and the name of the SS Caprice visible in every photo. Here they come! Get moving! Do you hear me!" he shouted.

Chapter Seven
The Perfect Host

Even with all the day's tensions, I still looked forward to our usual pre-dinner cocktail hour. Except, it occurred before the second seating in the dining room on this particular evening.

While I was hanging over the railing of the lower deck to view the hoisting of David's marlin, Walter found a new hideaway cocktail bar that none of us had frequented. He intended to make it his own personal property for the rest of our trip.

The bar was small with eight barstools and two tables. It sat sixteen to twenty people at the most, plus one bartender. For some reason, the bar wasn't listed on the printed brochure of the ship's facilities. Most of the bar's customers were ship workers, which explained its omission from the ship's brochure.

While waiting for the captain to hoist the thousand-pound marlin onto the loading dock for the inevitable photograph, I visited Patrick's bar, where I had once found him tapping away on Roger Danbury, Attorney at Law's, typewriter.

A different bartender was on duty, but the same young girl and married man huddled in a dark corner, holding each other close. Patrick wasn't there. For some reason, I suddenly felt lonely, so I left. I knocked on Patrick's cabin door, but there was no answer. Back on the pier, the fish had been photographed to within an inch of its now drying skin. The first photograph was of the fish being weighed. Then another of David pointing to the weight. Then another of him standing next to his disgusted grandmother, who seemed to think the fish was still alive. Followed by a photograph of the Captain of the SS Caprice, David, his grandmother, and the fish. Then the captain and crew of the fishing boat. By this time, Mrs. Winton had ordered cocktails and smelling salts to be delivered to the pier before she fainted.

The giant marlin carcass was then pushed through an opening in the side of the SS Caprice—presumably into a freezer. The scale disappeared. A long, low blast of the air horn sounded, followed by four short blasts, and the SS Caprice set sail for Puerto Vallarta at 6:30 pm, an hour-and-a-half late.

Patrick delivered his finished "introduction" for Mrs. Winton to read at dinner that night. Walter said very little during the dinner, but he did compliment David on his day's catch. He suggested that David be photographed riding on the back of the sea monster as if he were riding a bronco bull in a rodeo.

For some reason, Walter was paying more attention to the troubled youth. While taking our seats for dinner, David insisted that he wanted to be seated to Walter's right, between the two of us. Patrick agreed most heartedly as it removed David from his side of the table. Walter and David continued their private conversation about fishing and riding horses throughout most of the evening. David didn't play with his food, much to the delight of his grandmother and Patrick.

I decided to spend the evening entertaining Mrs. Winton.

"Have you ever been to Puerto Vallarta before, Mr. Karr?" she asked, fussing across the table with a dinner napkin to wipe a smudge from David's pudgy face.

"I hear that Hollywood is going to make Puerto Vallarta the film capital of all Mexico," said Patrick, as he crossed his knife and fork on his plate.

I noticed that our waiter for the evening had spent a considerable amount of time catering to Patrick Dennis and little to the rest of us.

"May I remove your plate, Mr. Dennis?" the waiter asked.

"*Oui,*" Patrick replied, glancing into the young waiter's face.

"Will there be anything else, Mr. Dennis?"

"Madam Winton? Would you care for some coffee perhaps, or a light liqueur?"

"Oh Patrick, I've had so many cocktails already, and with the wine reduced within the *boeuf bourguignon,* I think not. It has been a long and exhausting day for me, so you must forgive me." She took his arm and drew him closer to whisper in his ear. "I'm sure you understand the trauma I have been through today. I've asked the ship's doctor to prepare two sedatives, one for David, and one for me, to insure a good night's rest. I slipped David's in his water glass when he wasn't looking, and I have taken mine already. I'm afraid it's 'beddy-bye' time for the two of us quite soon. I'll make it up to you wonderful boys tomorrow. Nightie-night," she said, as the captain assisted her with David lagging behind to her quarters.

"She's going to sleep a good, deep sleep, tonight," I said. "I saw David switching the water glasses with her earlier, and he's only been drinking his Coke all evening."

"Do you think we should notify the captain?" Walter asked. But we all knew what the answer would be as Patrick raised his glass in salute to Walter and me. We all said it at the same time ... "No!"

Walter took us to his newly found, hidden away cocktail lounge. It was still early, and most of the dinner crew were still cleaning the restaurants and dining rooms and setting up for the next morning's breakfast.

Patrick suggested taking one of the small tables away from the door. With only one bartender and no cocktail waiter, we were surprised to have our drinks delivered by none other than Patrick's favorite waiter from the dining room. "Gentlemen, be my guests," he said with a flashing smile in Patrick's direction.

Word had spread of Patrick's fame as a writer. The three of us were constantly stopped so that Patrick could flourish his pen in a broad signature on anything available.

"I wouldn't mind toting a pile of your books around as we tour the ship," Walter offered.

"Mrs. Winton was kind enough to order a large supply of each of my three published books and has informed me that they are waiting for me at the El Colonial Hotel in Puerto Vallarta," Patrick whispered as he leaned over the small table. "Selling those books is going to be my cash flow after I jump ship."

"Then you really are determined to leave us here on our marvelous journey into the mystic land of Mexico," I said. "Do you plan on leaving IOUs to everyone you have borrowed money from? What about Edith Winton and her pile of books at the hotel? If she bought the books, she had to pay retail for them at some bookstore. How many did she order? I bought a paperback copy of *Auntie Mame,* and I think it set me back about $.60."

"Oh, *contraire,* my dear boy. I do not bother with those reduced-size, flimsy, printed paperback things. Only hardcover copies with dust jackets and photographs. Why, *Auntie Mame* in true book form would cost at least $3.50 per copy."

"I know you tend to enlarge upon the truth, Patrick, but you just said 'three' books. We know you've written *Auntie Mame,* but have you taken to gluing your photograph on the back of F. Scott Fitzgerald's or James Michener's novels and passing them off as your own?"

"Obviously, you are not literate in fine writing, Raub. I have written two books under the name of Virginia Rowans, *Oh What a Wonderful Wedding* and *House Party.* Both are dynamite books, and written under the alias of a woman, or *nom de plume.* Oh, I shall have plenty of books to sell, but first I will have to buy Walter several cocktails while he teaches me the intrinsic value of the Mexican peso. In the United States, coins that are in circulation are fractional divisions of a dollar bill, but here in the land of Aztecan mysteries and aggressive prostitutes, the filthy things can be centavos or the equivalent of the even filthier paper money. I have a pile of those small ridiculous coins, and now I find out that some of them are worth big dollars or pesos. Oh, Raub, I need a keeper to stay here in Mexico."

I had suffered enough for the day. I was about to leave when Patrick began one of his stories about visiting a pygmy tribe in Africa when he was in the American Field Service.

In Patrick's telling of his story, he performed diplomatic work during the war. In truth, he was an ambulance driver. Patrick had difficulty getting his ambulance to reverse without sticking his head out the driver's window and yelling to everyone to get out of the way. "There I was in the very bottom tip of Africa, an *aide de camp* to General Rushmolderman. We were constantly travelling between Cape Town, Pretoria, and Bloemfontein. German spies were everywhere. I may have killed a few in those days, but that is neither here nor there. After all, it was World War II, you know. After trekking through the sandy desert, our caravan was ambushed outside a little village. We had no water, and our camels had all died."

At this point, a food server asked where in South Africa were these vast expanses of drifting sand between Cape Town, Bloemfontein, and Pretoria, where there were excellent roads. The server also pointed out that there were no shootings or killings in South Africa during World War II.

I decided to stay and hear the end of Patrick's story. Walter was glued to his chair.

The best part of the story was where Patrick described how he pulled the pygmy princess, Kaflinga, from a crocodile-infested river while holding off and killing a squad of twenty Nazi sharpshooters. "Her father, Chief Wambutu, gave me a solid gold medal with his image on it, as big as a tea saucer, and so heavy it caused a bruise on my chest. I kept it for years but donated it to the African League for Decency and Reconstruction."

And on and on he went. The bar had never enjoyed such a rousing turnout and profits. Off-duty waiters carried empty beer bottles and glasses to the bar, where the lone bartender continued mixing his wares and serving to the eager and thirsty customers.

When Patrick described Glicktu, the usurper of the pygmy kingdom (complete with the clicking sound of the lips and glottal stop), and the fierce attack on Patrick's life, I had to leave.

I left the two of them, the best of friends, clinking glasses with waiters, engine stokers, laundry experts, mid-shipmen, and even officers from the deck. Then I heard Patrick's voice, *"Mi amigos,* your entire bar tabs for tonight are on me! Such is the love I have for this ship, the *SS Carnival* or *Capricious* or whatever the name of this manner of conveyance is."

Weak and intoxicated, I didn't venture on deck to view the beautiful Mexican moonlight on the ocean's blue waters. Instead, I chose Mrs. Winton's traveling route down the long corridors, balancing myself on the heavy oak railings. I was totally intoxicated and singing at the top of my lungs, "Oh, Virginia Rowans! What a wonderful wedding and house party you have given!"

Somehow, I managed to undress and fall onto my bed. Walter was nowhere to be found, and at this point, I could care less.

My final thought for the night was about an 1860 Riverboat scene on the Mississippi River where Patrick, as the compulsive gambler, faces off against Cary Grant, who is forced to pay up for his losses at the gaming table.

"I warn ya, sir," the cigar-smoking mustached Patrick said to Cary Grant. "We river people don't take tah cheap greenhorns like you. Best yah pay up what yah owe an' be on yo way."

A very youthful Randolph Scott stepped forward and put his hands on Patrick's shoulder. "There ain't gonna' be no shootin' heeya tonight," he said pulling his Meerschaum smoking pipe from his mouth. "Best yah all go back home."

That's when I passed out into my own dreams of stable, clean, prudish Seattle.

Chapter Eight

Oh, Capitan, the Troops Have Deserted!

Once out in the open sea and away from Mazatlan, the captain increased the ship's speed by four knots. Our departure had been delayed due to David's marlin catch, and he wanted to maintain a good log record of arrival and departure times.

Surprisingly, there was no major disturbance during the night from David. Edith Winton slept soundly even when security officers made a late-night visit to her suite of rooms to convince David that smoking cigars on his open lanai caused discomfort to the passengers in the next-door suite.

The cigars, stolen from the captain's quarters earlier in the evening, proved his undoing. He was now violently ill and throwing up.

Rather than disturb Mrs. Winton, the crew carried the troublesome youth to the infirmary, bedded him on an observation gurney, and locked the only door into or out of the room.

I awoke at 7:30 that morning. I saw the colorful vast Mexico coastline speeding past out of the open porthole. Walter was nowhere to be seen, and his bed had not been slept in. I rang for the room porter and asked if anyone had seen him, but this crew had come on duty at 5:30, and no one had seen him.

Walter was probably intoxicated and sleeping it off in Patrick's room. Or perhaps he had found a drinking companion in a fellow passenger or crew member for the night.

I shaved, showered, and dressed. The SS Caprice was scheduled to arrive in Puerto Vallarta in five hours.

At breakfast, I was the only diner at the large dining table. The waiter who had shown so much interest in Patrick during last night's dinner and later at the private bar brought a large carafe of steaming hot coffee. "Señor Patrick is enjoying his morning meal in his cabin, and Mr. Healy will be joining you shortly. Mrs. Winton and little David are indisposed this morning but have invited all of you to her stateroom cabin at noon for a luncheon before we dock at Puerto Vallarta. Señor Patrick also has asked that after your morning breakfast, you join him in the main salon. He has organized a mid-day gathering of his most adoring fans and has promised to read excerpts from his upcoming book. Finally, Mr. Healy asked me to inform you that he has spoken to the ship's purser, and by use of the ship-to-shore radio communications, he has made suitable arrangements for the rental of an automobile to tour the city of Puerto Vallarta."

'Oh, just great,' I thought. 'Walter's a terrible driver, and with Patrick coming from New York City, I doubt if he even has a driver's license.'

I finished my meager breakfast and returned to our room, but Walter wasn't there. I knocked on Patrick's cabin door but received no answer. So I went to the main salon, where I expected to find Patrick with a group of his adoring fans, but the salon was also empty. It was too early for the bars to open. I feared that Walter, if not both of them, had a "snoot full" last night after I left the employees' bar.

I wandered around the decks and spoke to the head purser about exchanging money onboard. Or would it be better to exchange it in Puerto Vallarta? He told me that on board I would get a better rate. Then he told me about Walter. "Yes, he paid his entire bill with his credit card, and it was a hefty one. He then took a $400 cash advance from the card, and said he had a lot of shopping to do in Puerto Vallarta. Are you also going to pay your bill at this time, Mr. Karr? I'll just have to open two new accounts for you guys to cover the rest of the trip to Acapulco and then all the way back to the states."

I assured him I was not paying my bill off at this time and to excuse me. I had to find Walter and find out what in the hell was going on!

It was just after one o'clock, and the second seating for lunch was over. Edith was seated alone at our table. "Oh, Raub, I'm so glad you came. Where is everybody? Nobody came for lunch, not even David, and he never misses a meal. What's going on? A room steward brought me a handful of envelopes for you and Walter from Patrick. Even David had one from Walter, and then the same steward came back and asked to take back the envelope addressed to Walter from Patrick. I haven't opened anything. I was waiting for someone to come tell me what this is all about. Why is everybody sending notes back and forth this morning?"

I spread the envelopes out before me. The first envelope was typed and addressed to me from Patrick. I surmised that this was Patrick's "Farewell, sorry about owing you so much money, we'll be in touch" and that he was jumping ship.

I was more interested in what Walter had written to me, being that I hadn't even talked to him since last night's bar soireé.

Dear Raub,

You know I have been worried about my job back in Seattle. Well, yesterday afternoon I called Best Apparel and talked to my old secretary, Judy. They hired a new personnel director, and she said they were going to let me go as soon as I got back from the boat trip. I really don't know what to do, but I sure don't want to go back to Seattle with no job.

Can you hold onto my stuff until I work something out? Patrick claims he will pay me to translate for him and stick with him until his agent gets him some more money. I don't really believe him about paying me, but what the heck. I've got about $1,300 in American money on me. I told Patrick that I only had about $400. Patrick says he has written you about what you should say on board after the boat *has sailed to Acapulco this evening. I need time to be by myself to think everything out. Hope you will understand. I'll be in touch.*

Thanks, Walter

I gave the envelope addressed to David from Walter to Edith and told her to give it to him.

"Raub, I'm worried about David. It isn't like him to miss a meal, and I haven't seen hide nor hair of him all day. Do you think he's with Walter? Maybe they plan on going ashore together once we dock. I'll bet that's it. He probably thinks I wouldn't allow him to go alone with Walter, but I would. That's it, I'm sure, but why would Walter write him a note if they were going together?" she asked, even more confused than usual.

"Edith, be sure to give David his envelope when he does appear. I must go to my cabin and see if Walter is there. I'm not going ashore until much later. I'll call you before I do, just to be sure you've found David and he's OK."

Walter had returned to our cabin. Everything he had brought with him for the trip was gone, except his heavy winter clothing from Seattle and San Francisco. All his luggage, shoes, socks, underwear, shirts, and pants were gone. The hangers he requested from our room steward were neatly hung in the now empty closet.

I felt alone and deserted, even though he had left another envelope for me that contained $100 for his share of the room steward's tip.

I was angry at the current events and tore open Edward Everett Tanner III's envelope to find a typed three-page letter/plea for me to follow and obey:

My Darling Raub,

I, who considers himself so glib with the flowing words, hardly know what to say, except that my heart is aching already, and I truly wish things were different, but they aren't. Walter and I have been talking, and we have decided to end the SS Caprice (isn't that name symbolic) ocean voyage and try our fortunes on dry land.

In order to pull this charade off on my part, I must ask and beg for your understanding and assistance. I have included the proper telephone numbers of those I wish notified of my disappearance. If you desire to keep it a mystery to everyone, then that's what it will be. I know and trust you, my good new friend, and whatever you tell them onboard will be fine and believable to forestall any involvement of the police.

Walter and I need time to think things out. I will sell everything I possess to accomplish this, even poor old Roger Danbury's typewriter if I have to. Walter has to find himself and stop his dangerous drinking, and I feel with both of us on extremely limited resources, he will be able to put his job failure behind him and become productive once again.

I know that you and poor Edith will never understand what we are doing but let us try.

You will be sailing tonight for Acapulco and in four days time, you will arrive back here in Puerto Vallarta on your return trip to Seattle.

Walter and I will find you somehow when the ship docks.

Fondly, Patrick

P.S. Walter and I are not going to the El Colonial Hotel to claim my books until tomorrow. I'm sure Edith has already forgotten about ordering and sending them.

Love and kisses!

I dropped onto Walter's empty bed, wondering what I should or should not tell those here on the boat. Then, there was a soft tap at my door. "David, good to see you. I hear you were ill last night after smoking the captain's cigars. Your grandmother has been looking for you and wonders why you missed lunch. If you haven't eaten, come on in. I missed lunch as well and was about to order a sandwich, but first you should call her and tell her that you're here with me and not onshore. You were planning on going ashore with Walter, weren't you?"

David settled in the desk chair and looked as if he were about to cry.

"Walter promised he would take you with him this afternoon to see Puerto Vallarta, but he ditched you, didn't he? He sent you a note, that your grandmother has at this very moment, but that's no excuse for his dumping you like that. But you have to understand Walter—He has a lot of problems. In fact, both he and Mr. Dennis are causing a lot of trouble for everybody. I'm glad you stopped by. Let's order a sandwich, and I will tell you what's really going on, but you must promise not to tell anyone. Do you agree?"

"I thought Walter was my friend. I don't have any friends on this stinkin' old boat, at least anybody my age, and yesterday it was kinda' fun talkin' to Walter about havin' our pictures taken ridin' that old marlin bareback. He sure knows a lot about horses."

"Yes, David, and he also knows a lot about little boys growing up without friends his own age. Walter only had his father and an older brother. He had to fend for himself, fix his own meals, and get himself to school on time. He had to take care of the house where they lived because both his father and brother had jobs. You know how fussy he is about his clothes. Well, he learned that from being alone all the time. He was very lonely when he was your age, but he couldn't do anything about it. Walter and I talked about you, and he came to the right conclusion about why you go against everything and everybody. You're not a mean-spirited kid. You just want some attention and someone to talk to. You pull all these stupid pranks just to get somebody to show they care about you. Walter couldn't do that when he was your age. He had too many responsibilities just staying alive, going to school, and keeping up the house for his dad."

"But why did he promise to take me with him when he was goes into Puerto Vallarta, and then stand me up? I waited a whole hour near the loading dock, but neither he nor Mr. Dennis showed up. I stole a passkey for all the rooms on the boat, and you know what I think? Mr. Dennis has jumped ship. I went to his cabin and there weren't nothing of his in the room. No clothes, no luggage, no nothin.' Why would he want to do that if the whole trip has been paid for by grandma, an' other than all his drinkin', everything was paid for until we get back to Seattle? Come to think of it, Raub, where are Walter's clothes? The closet's empty like Mr. Dennis's."

"David, if I had all the answers, I'd tell you, but I don't. I don't know what Walter has written to you, but right now, we must do a little protecting of everybody until we can sort this all out. I want you to call your grandmother and tell her that you are with me for the afternoon, and that we are staying onboard and *not* going into Puerto Vallarta. If she asks you, tell her that Mr. Dennis and Walter did go into town to do something, but you don't know what. Please don't tell her that they're both gone. I'll let everybody know once we're out at sea. I'll tell her they decided to spend the next four days in Puerto Vallarta to do something special. Oh, I don't know right now what, but it'll come to me. I'll tell her they'll be back on board when we come through Puerto Vallarta next Wednesday on our way back from Acapulco. This is very important, David. Will you help me?"

"I don't know, Raub. I don't trust anybody anymore, not even Grandma. She asked me what I wanted to do with my marlin, an' I told her I wanted to have it stuffed. It's the biggest and bestest thing I ever did in my life an' I'd a found someplace to put it or even give it tah somebody who wanted it, but she promised me we'd take care of it back in Seattle, but she lied. When Walter and I went down inta the hold to get our pictures taken riding it bareback, the fish was gone. The captain dumped it in the ocean once we went past the 12-mile zone. They said that was his orders, an' they just opened the steerage door and pushed my fish out inta the ocean. I don't trust nobody no more, not even you. I'm goin' back to my cabin. I don't feel like no sandwich."

"Think it over about helping Patrick and Walter, will you? Will I see you at dinner tonight, or what should I expect?"

"I don't know. I want to read Walter's letter to me."

That evening at dinner, I sat alone for almost an hour, waiting for Edith and David to arrive. They never came, nor did I receive a message from them.

Captain Cartwright made his obligatory rounds, greeting people in the dining room that night, pausing briefly at my empty table. "Well, Mr. Karr, it seems your friends have made a mess of this cruise for Mrs. Winton. You might as well know, she has reported the disappearance of both of them to the Mexican police as well as the American Consulate. Actually, your friend, Mr. Healy, has done nothing wrong and has acted on his own in joining Mr. Dennis or Tanner, whatever you wish to call him. It is Mr. Dennis who has attempted to deceive Mrs. Winton out of a considerable amount of money by taking the books she shipped to Puerto Vallarta for him, as well as her paying the attorney fellow, Roger Danbury, the money for the cabin fare. It's a sizable amount, you know. She said to tell you that you are welcome to use her table for the balance of the cruise, but she and David will be having all their meals in her cabin for the next eleven days, the balance of the cruise. I only wish I'd known how little David felt about that marlin. I would have spoken up to Mrs. Winton about dumping it in the ocean. He said that Mr. Healy lied to him and had no intention of being his friend. It's going to take a lot to calm him down over all of this."

"Captain, I thank you for your honesty, and if I may do the same, I must tell you that I do not believe either Mr. Healy or Mr. Dennis have any intention of returning to the ship once we dock in Puerto Vallarta on the return voyage. If you would convey to Mrs. Winton that I shall attempt to cover any onboard charges incurred by Mr. Dennis, but unfortunately, I am not able to pay the entire amount at this moment."

"No need to worry about that, Mr. Karr. She talked to the purser this afternoon, and the matter has been settled."

We arrived in Acapulco, and I made only one short trip into the city. On the return trip to Puerto Vallarta, I walked the entire pier and stood near the gangplank for an eternity, but neither Walter nor Patrick appeared.

At Mazatlan, Los Angeles, and San Francisco, I spent most of my time in my cabin reading some of the materials that Patrick had left behind. His untipped room steward brought them to me, thinking they might be of some value, but they were only very brief outlines of short stories and vague ideas for future writing. I paid him $20 for the pile, and once on the docks of Seattle Harbor, I felt I had indeed heard the end of Patrick Dennis and Walter Healy.

I heard nothing from either of them until the beginning of March when a postcard arrived from Acapulco from Patrick. He was in trouble, not with the police, but moneywise, and he had lost contact with Walter. Could I help? I left for Acapulco the following morning.

Chapter Nine
Hotel Molino de Agua

Years of neglect had led to the decay of buildings on the seafront around the *Bahia de Acapulco*. The lobby of the *Molina de Agua Hotel,* below the *mercado,* resembled a local bar or cantina. The hotel rooms were up a narrow wooden staircase. Even the *asiento,* seating area, was only accessible through a low swinging gate controlled by the hotel owner or whoever was working behind the counter.

The *asiento,* or *salon de fumer,* held approximately forty people. A collection of unmatched furniture, consisting of overstuffed wingback chairs and broken wicker seats, was scattered around. Two large bare windows looked out onto the street. The bay windows provided additional seating on the wide, chipped concrete windowsills. Although, the window frames, sashes, and glass had long since been removed.

If it rained, then the rain came into the *salon de fumer.* One window seat was cushioned with a folded Mexican blanket. The other, a car or truck's leather bench seat with metal springs and torn leather, threatened to catch the flesh or clothing of anyone careless enough to sit on it.

The *Molino,* true to its name, had been a grain mill at one time—a gristmill stone rested in the weeds and cactus plants at the entrance to the hotel. Its source of power for turning the massive carved stone was a mystery. The hotel's location was some distance from the piers and docks of the *Bahia de Acapulco.*

As I entered the hotel, a man sat behind the counter, reading his morning newspaper. He was a man in his early 50s with graying sideburns. His arms were thick and covered with twisted mats of black hair, even on his short, stubby knuckles. He must have done heavy lifting most of his life.

"*Buenos dias,*" I said in my best-learned *Ingles/Español* Spanish. "*Estoy buscando al Señor Dennis.*"

"*Me debe mucho dinero.*" The man behind the desk spits out the words as if he wanted the entire world to know that Dennis hadn't paid his bill.

"I will pay his bill after I see him."

"*Número cinco,*" he answered.

"*Donde está el ascensor?*" I asked, searching for the elevator.

"*Sin ascensor subir escaleras.*" The man pointed to the rickety stairs. American *perezosos!*"

"*Gracias.*" I replied.

I thought the hotel room, Number 5, would be on the second floor. But that entire floor of eight rooms was rented out to scantily clad women. Some sat with their legs dangling over the windowsill, attempting to lure a tourist, man, or even a young boy.

"*Quieres dormir conmigo. Soy muy bonito, no soy yo?*" one offered.

"*Si,* you are very beautiful, but I cannot sleep with you right now," I replied.

"*Tengo que hacer aquí con el Señor Dennis. Gracias de todas formas.*" Disappointed, she pointed to the stairs leading up to the third floor.

As I continued up the squeaky steps to the third floor, I heard babies crying and a bitter argument between two of the *putas* arguing over who was to service the drunken Mexican in his fieldwork pants.

A woman sat on the landing of the third floor dressed entirely in black. The arms on her wobbly wheelchair held her emaciated body. Her hair was dyed black, fashioned neatly in the net snood at the back of her head. Her gown, which showed pale white skin on her shoulders and flesh-sagging arms, was most likely a mourning dress. A black lace shawl was draped over her head and bare shoulders. Her woven gloves were fingerless, exposing ten gnarled fingers, one hand grasping a black fan, the other a smoldering cigarette. A long black ribbon was strung around the jowl of her neck. Tucked in the slight cleavage of her breast was a single white pearl suspended from the black ribbon.

She resembled the Empress Consort Charlotte, awaiting her husband, Emperor Don Maximiliano I, the former ex-Archduke of Austria, who, with the backing of Napoleon III and a wild tribe of Mexican monarchists, had once sought to revive the Mexican monarchy but failed.

"*Buenos dias, Señora,*" I said softly.

There was no window on this landing, and a single lightbulb that threw a sliver of light onto her black *mantilla*.

She didn't reply, simply bowed her head an inch or two in recognition.

"*Estoy buscando Señor Dennis,*" I asked.

"*Número cinco* is *Señor Denneeees's* room. He no live there. My son-in-law lock door. Señor Denneeees owe much money. Son-in law want money, keep lock on door. I like Señor Deneeees. He sleep with puta in room on second floor. Night manager sleep on job. I give Señor Denneeees key to his room. He take many things and go with puta. He wear big *sombrero* when leave hotel. Señor Deneeees sell me book he write. I pay $200 peso. Señor Denneeees muy funny man, tell story good, make everyone laugh."

I was desperate to find Patrick, to warn him about seeking lodging in another flophouse in the *mercado* district. Filthy, cheap flophouses stayed in touch with each other, warning each other of deadbeats, destitute American college students, and sometimes those wanted by the FBI.

I bid farewell to the old Empress Charlotte on the third floor and passed the waiting *putas* on the second floor. The manager behind the desk turned out to be the old woman's son-in-law, the proprietor of the *Molina de Agua Hotel*. He was swarthy and brutish by nature. He pressured the girls on the second floor to earn enough to pay their rent. The girls were expected to secure a gentleman from the streets on their own. He was not their pimp or *alcahuete*, but merely the renter of rooms by the hour at twice the rate Patrick had been paying for the entire night.

The manager looked pleased with himself after sending me up two flights of stairs only to find that Number 5 was padlocked.

"Your friend, Mr. Denneeees, owe much rent money. He cannot return and collect his possessions until entire amount is paid. We do not take credit cards."

"How much does he owe?" I asked. "Señor Dennis informed me that he checked into this dump last Friday afternoon, March 12th. Today is Monday the 15th, and the notice on your posted sign states that rents begin at 2 o'clock in the afternoon. Therefore, his rent is for only three days—Friday, Saturday, and Sunday. Señor Dennis also informed me that the daily rate was $24 pesos per day, and that he had paid in cash for the first day. Is that correct?"

"It is not correct, Señor. This is quality hotel, and the rate is $35 pesos per day. Señor Denneeees checked in on Friday before 2 o'clock. Therefore, he owes for four days. I have no record that he paid the first day. He also owe the standard cleaning charge of $50 pesos. I insist that the total bill, $190 pesos, be paid before I release to you his possessions. Everything is locked in room."

"Insist all you want, Señor. I see no sign posted that this establishment charges a cleaning fee, and as for his not giving you a one-day deposit as your sign requests, you can simply go to blazes or Tijuana, for all I care. I have in my hand $75 pesos. Take it or leave it. I consider the amount fair, as he may have checked in before the 2 o'clock time. What is it to be, or shall I use the telephone at the corner to summon the *policia?* I am sure you would find it difficult removing the twenty-some ladies now doing business on the second floor before the police arrived."

He reached out his open hand for the money.

"A receipt, please. Then you may have your money. Give me the padlock key, and I will inspect his room, although I am sure there's nothing in it."

He scribbled the receipt and signed it with a flourish, grabbed his ring of keys, and was halfway up the first flight of stairs by the time I could join him. He fumbled with his keys outside of room number five and opened the lock. "*Aye, Caramba!*" he yelled. "Where is all Señor Denneeees's things? His clothing? Suitcase? and books he brought?"

On a small desk near the open window sat an envelope marked as coming from the Dorchester Hotel in London. It had my name on it. I scooped it up and handed the hotel manager his money.

The old Mexican woman wheeled her ancient wheelchair to what had once been Patrick's room. Her withered hand flicked a long ash from her burning cigarette. She took an exceptionally long drag on the cigarette and then spit in the direction of her son-in-law. "*Picaro, ees crook!*" she yelled. "He steal many things from Señor Denneeees. He make youngest daughter, Estancia, work as *puta* on second floor." This time her saliva sailed through the air and landed on the son-in-law's trouser leg. Señor Denneeees take Estancia from this terrible place. Señor Denneeees good man."

As I passed this "Empress Charlotte," she grabbed my hand and squeezed it tight. "Tell Señor Denneeees *bueno* and *muchas gracias.*"

The son-in-law gestured toward the door that I should leave. "Business is finished here," he snorted as he relocked the bedroom door.

"I'll take that receipt now, if you don't mind," I said, snatching it from his chubby fist.

Chapter Ten

I Have Found Patrick, But Where is Walter?

I recognized Patrick's distinctive handwriting and opened the letter. The blue envelope was identified as coming from the Dorchester Hotel on Park Lane in London. However, the cream-colored embossed stationery with the gold border came from Claridge's on Brook Street, Mayfair, London.

Sunday Evening, the 14th

My Dearest Raubito,

Oh, the horrors of it all to be penniless in such a ghastly place like Mexico. It is filled with robbers, crooks, and, yes, whores. But then, aren't we all?

I had to flee this decrepit place for yet another cockroach-infested domicile, mainly because of the thievery of the manager/owner. I have caught him going through my meager possessions, and worst of all, he has stolen the last of my American cigarettes.

Did you, by chance, bring any of those delightful black cigarettes you smoke? Señorita Estancia and I are shacked up in the Bellas Artes Hotel on the Malecon.

Come quickly, we have not eaten in days.

Hasta luego,

Señor Danbury Abogado

The Bellas Artes Hotel was even worse than the *Molino de Agua*. The stucco building with large boulders embedded in its walls consisted of two floors of glassless windows. Hung in the windows were freshly laundered articles of clothing and bed linens in the sweltering Acapulco afternoon sun.

I entered the hotel lobby to find Patrick surrounded by a large group of Mexican children who were all yelling and laughing at the same time.

On a visit to the hotel's only ground floor toilet, Patrick found a dispensing machine. If you inserted 50 centavos, you could buy a brightly colored packet of *profilácticos*, condoms.

Patrick considered Mexican coins worthless, preferring the weathered and torn paper money in his wallet. So, he used the coins to buy condoms. He was now delighting the children by inflating the prophylactic and making long skinny "wiener" dogs or *perro pachons,* Dachshunds.

"What took you so long?" he asked sarcastically.

"I didn't know there was a specific time I was to come to your aid and rescue you, Patrick. Do forgive me," I responded with equal sarcasm.

Patrick approached the hotel registration desk, an old wood-topped table with its registration book open, displaying the signatures of its guests. There was only one legible signature, 'Mr. Jones from Los Angeles, California,' the rest were all "X" signatures with no destination cities.

Patrick took the fountain pen and signed the name "Señorita Estancia" with a flourish.

Patrick asked the clerk what the daily rate was and told him that the señorita would be staying for a week. "Figure out how much that is in their 'funny' money and pay the man, Raubito. Señorita Estancia has taken care of me and provided for my welfare. It is only proper that I repay her by paying her rent for the week. And before you offer one of your snide remarks, Raub ... yes, we have been sleeping together. I find her delightful, and she has eased my tensions of living in this dreadful part of the world ever so much. You wouldn't have a decent American cigarette on you, would you, my boy? I have been informed that a significant amount of money is being transferred from my publisher to the *cambista* at the Banco de Mexico, $10,000 pesos to be precise. Have no fear, Raub, you shall be paid back every centavo you have spent on me."

"Believe me when I say that I have no fear of the repayment, as Mr. Edmonds of your publishing firm has entrusted me to accept the $10,000 pesos, pay your bills, get you back to your writing and, in general, keep you out of trouble. And furthermore, my expenses and total reimbursements for loans, hotel bills, cab fares, food, and liquor, is not coming out of your $10,000 pesos. Mr. Edmunds has paid me those sums separately from your earnings account of sold books. He is personally loaning you the $10,000 pesos. Why, I have no idea. He appears to be a sane and intelligent man, but then he's the expert in the publishing world and seems to think you're a good investment. Why, I will never understand. But first, Patrick, I have some questions. Where is Walter?"

"My boy, if I knew, I would tell you. You know I adore that boy and would do anything for him, but he simply disappeared one evening, and I have never heard from him since."

"From the last address I sent money to, the two of you were renting a house at *Cumbre de Montaña,* up in the hillside above the city. Was Walter still living with you when you were kicked out of there for nonpayment of rent?"

"I think he was. Yes, he was still with me because we checked into the Fairmont Acapulco Princess. Walter discovered he still had one credit card left, and besides, we were hungry."

"Your stay at the Fairmont Princess lasted exactly three days before they demanded their money. Walter's credit card had been denied. Was Walter with you when you were evicted from the hotel?" I demanded.

My patience with Patrick was wearing thin. He felt no responsibility towards Walter, even though he had borrowed his last peso to buy cigarettes. They had been living by their wits ever since I left Mexico aboard the SS Caprice and returned to Seattle.

That was over four months ago after Walter telephoned Seattle and discovered that he had lost his job with Best Apparel. 'Gross Negligence and Failure to Perform his Duties,' were the reasons for his dismissal. Walter was excellent in his position as personnel director of the store. He enjoyed dressing smartly for the job and presented himself perfectly at the store functions. Walter's problem was his lunchtime drinking. At first, his staff noticed that his one-hour lunch break lasted an hour and a half, then two hours. His secretary refused to book appointments for him until after 3:00p.m. Walter telephoned his office to see how things were going, but soon he failed to return at all some days.

When he requested vacation time to sail on the SS Caprice, management decided changes had to be made. The way he discovered his dismissal may have been cruel, but the store settled a one month's salary on him for his severance.

Patrick had long planned to jump ship before Walter decided to do the same. Now Walter was a free spirit, free from responsibilities of having an apartment, a car, and paying bills—a handsome young man with a winning smile, a love of life, and... a drinking problem.

I didn't tell Patrick that I had arrived in Acapulco two days earlier. I considered telling him. But receiving no assistance in finding Walter, I thought it was equal justice to make Patrick suffer some of the indignities Walter was going through without a peso to his name.

All five hotels, with rankings from minus two to one star, were paid in full, along with several restaurants on Walter's credit-card charges. In all, it came to $12,000 for the two of them. I didn't break down each bill to see who charged or ordered what. In my mind, they were both equally responsible for the bills, but Patrick Dennis would be the one to pay for all of it.

"I have made reservations for you back at the Fairmont. The accommodations will not be as grand as when you and Walter stayed there a month ago, but the room has been paid for the entire month in advance. Gather up your boxes of clothing and junk and bring it with you. Say goodbye to Señorita Estancia, if you like, or maybe you would like to bring her along to the Fairmont Acapulco Princess. The sight of the two of you walking through the lobby being stared at by well-heeled, actual paying guests, should be quite a sight," I snarled.

"Raubito, what is the matter with you? You know I adore you, and that I respect you as the most trusted critic of my writing. What have I done that has turned you against me?"

"Everything is very convenient for you, isn't it, Patrick? It was convenient that you forgot about your wife, Louise, and your two children, Michael and Betsy. Mr. Edmunds, your agent, said that your wife is hysterical with worry about where you are and that you are okay. I guess you meant to telephone them between cocktails on one of these long, delightful, Mexican evenings. By the way, the Roger Danbury boat ticket affair and charges were finally dropped. As you know, Edith Winton coughed up the money to pay him back. Funny Mr. Danbury, who I am sure is a very diligent attorney, seems they have forgotten that you still have his typewriter in your possession, unless you've sold it. But you have forgotten someone who also adored you... Walter. You're despicable, Patrick Dennis."

"Despicable or not, I truly want to help you find Walter. The last I heard he was hanging out at the El Colonial Hotel near the paragliding stand. I saw him there several times. Surprisingly, a couple times he was stone-cold sober, and the Mexican boys let him go up in the sails. Walter is a good talker and brought in considerable new business for that kite-flying thing."

"Well, Patrick, before I get you settled into your new home for at least the next month, we are making a side trip over to the El Colonial Hotel. I am dead set on finding Walter today, or I may be 'dead set' on making your stay at the Fairmont Princess for a shorter period... say like, for only one day. I can just see the headlines, 'Noted Writer Found Dead in Mexican Hotel.' If your room is on a high floor, I may simply push you off the lanai. Otherwise, as I'm younger and stronger than you, I might hold your head in a toilet long enough for you to kick the can!"

We took a taxicab to the El Colonial Hotel. Unfortunately, the driver didn't get out of the cab to help Patrick and me with his belongings. "A little help here, Señor!" yelled Patrick, but the mustachioed driver refused to help.

Patrick's personal possessions had increased considerably since the days of the SS Caprice. He now owned a pair of matching leather luggage cases with heavy-duty straps around their girth. The cases weighed a ton. They contained all his writing and reference materials, and what books he had left for sale to his adoring fans. There was also a smaller Samsonite case of questionable age and condition, which contained his clothing and bathroom supplies. He also carried four large plastic bags. They weren't heavy, just awkward in the back seat of the taxicab.

"You will forgive me, Patrick, but if we do finally check you into your hotel, I will be walking at least twenty feet behind you. I'll tip the porters to carry your—excuse the expression—luggage for you, but I refuse to carry plastic bags. Have you been stealing sheets and pillows from the various lodgings where you stayed and then sneaked out without paying your bill?"

"Hardly, my boy. The bags are Walter's complete *accoutrements*. He sold most of his wardrobe and luggage. The shoe collection brought a veritable fortune, and we dined and drank for days."

I arranged with a hotel porter to hold Patrick's possessions while we looked for Walter.

"There he is!" Patrick exclaimed excitedly. "He's seated at the bar."

"What bar? I only see an enormous swimming pool with all the umbrellas and cabanas around it."

"Look in the direct center of the swimming pool. That's where the bar is." Patrick explained as if I were an idiot.

As we got closer to the pool, it became clear that the bar was in the center of the pool. I wondered if the bar came first and the pool built around it, or vice versa? Either way, the drinking customers were gathered in groups around the counters, a foot above the water level.

To get to the bar, we would have to change into bathing suits, enter the large peanut-shaped pool, and swim to the center. A runway ramp of poured concrete provided the bartenders and wait staff access. Young Mexican boys swarmed under the soaring ramp to look up the short skirts of cocktail waitresses. They walked back and forth over the ramp, placing orders and delivering refreshments to the sun seekers seated around the pool.

The bar was clover-shaped. Customers sat on submerged concrete barstools, their elbows resting on the mosaic countertops, clutching their plastic glasses with spears of pineapple, cherries, and olives. Each drink was adorned with brightly colored straws and paper umbrellas. Mexican mariachi music blasted from the outdoor speakers hanging from palm trees.

"But how do they pay for their drinks? The hotel guests had to swim out to the bar to be served. They're all wearing bathing suits. Where do they put the money?"

"You sign for everything at this hotel. All you have to do is show your brass hotel room key," said Patrick.

"Well, I see Walter swilling them away. He's wearing a bathing suit and a pair of sunglasses, and I would suspect that's about all. Good God! Look at his hair! He looks like a beatnik, and he's so tanned. His skin looks like old shoe leather. How do we get his attention? I'm going to walk over to the bar on that ramp."

"You can't. That's for the help only. Besides, you'd be standing next to one of the bartenders once you got there.

"*Señorita, por favor,*" Patrick called out, sounding like a seasoned Acapulco native. "*Papel y lápiz.* Can we afford a cocktail, Raub, or are we to die of thirst in this boiling hot Mexican sun? Walter seems to be involved in some sort of a game at the bar. I have asked the waitress for paper and a pencil to write him a note. You have that look on your face that you're about to yell out his name, but that might not be wise, especially if Walter is working his money-earning 'pea under the shell' game. No, a note is much better. Yelling is so *déclassé.*"

Eventually, our drinks arrived along with a smiling Walter, who, other than the flowing mop of hair and leather-brown tanned skin, looked the same as always, except he was smiling his broad toothy grin. He said something to our waitress in machine-gun Spanish and handed her a 50-peso note. She blushed an acceptance along with a *"muchas gracias."*

Walter slumped into a deck chair, and the three of us calmly sipped our first cocktail together in almost five months. There was a long silence. I had a million things I wanted to tell Walter and questions I wanted answered from Patrick. However, I waited for the two of them to sort out whatever was going on between them before I beat them both to a pulp for what they put me through.

"Patrico, you're losing more and more of what little hair you have," said Walter smugly.

"Si, mi amigo, and I notice your constant hand tremors have subsided ... somewhat. 'DTs,' I believe they are called. Other than your brown, suitcase-leather skin and that mop of sun-bleached hair, you look the same. I've missed you, you know."

"And I have missed you also, Patrick."

I lifted my glass. *"Amigos,* may I make a toast to the three of us and the SS Caprice."

Chapter Eleven
Walter's New Beginning

Day turned into night as we reminisced at the El Colonial Hotel poolside. Patrick talked of his success in accomplishing a sizeable amount of serious writing. He even recited a few storylines and significant points of one of his in-progress books.

At first, Walter was vague about how he survived. Finally, he admitted to being attracted to American male college tourists who were flush with cash. And how they fell victim to his "pea under the shell" sleight-of-hand game.

I started telling them of my futile efforts in tracking the two of them down, but they were more interested in hearing about each other's adventures. Some of their stories were outrageous. Some were sad and pitiful, while others were out-and-out criminal.

It was now nighttime with the gas torches and a mariachi band strolling from table to table. Neither Patrick nor I had eaten since breakfast.

A distinguished Mexican gentleman in a pristine white suit, light-blue dress shirt, and dark-blue necktie approached our table. He spoke to Walter on the side, away from the two of us.

"What's that all about?" I asked.

"Raub, Patrick, this is Señor Julio Gomez. He is the General Manager of the El Colonial Hotel. He has reminded me that swimsuits are not permitted as evening attire in the bar after 8:00 p.m. I am most sorry, Señor Gomez. I shall retire to the employees' lockers at once and change. Señor Gomez, this is my oldest friend from Seattle, Washington ... Raub Karr. And this is the illustrious author, Patrick Dennis, from New York City. I shall attempt to convince him to hold a lecture or two about his books here at the El Colonial Hotel. Raub, while I am changing, please order some of the seafood *hors d'oeuvres*. The shrimp wrapped in bacon with water chestnuts is excellent. I'll be right back."

As Walter left to change his clothes in, of all places, the employees' locker room, another round of drinks arrived with the waitress informing us that they were from Señor Gomez, the General Manager.

"Remind me to ask Walter if he wishes the balance of his Seattle clothing delivered to his employees' locker room, or what?" sniped Patrick.

Walter returned, dressed in a pristine white tailored suit, light-blue dress shirt, and dark-blue tie. He was a younger vision of Señor Gomez. His thick, long black hair, with its sun-tipped ends, was brushed back smooth and flat against his temples, ending in a short nubby pigtail or a queue at the back of his head. His suit pocket held a folded blue handkerchief. Below it was a gold nameplate with his name and 'Relaciones Publicas.'

"Walter, you have a job here at the hotel? What in the hell do you know about public relations?" I asked.

"Nothing. That's probably why they hired me. I've been writing to various fraternities and sororities in the states and inviting the college kids down for vacations, especially the Easter break. In almost all the fraternities in Southern California, I am known as 'El Bandito.' I haven't lost one challenge yet with those college kids, either drinking or with my shell game. Señor Gomez allows me to keep my own hours. I can do anything I want, as long as the college kids keep coming and filling his rooms."

"Where are you living? It looks as if you're working for food and drinks. Do you have any money?"

"Barely enough to get by, but the night clerks let me sleep in vacant rooms, but I'm afraid I'll get caught by Señor Gomez. He thinks I'm paying for all my food, room, and drinks, but the staff is giving me everything for free. I can draw big crowds to the restaurants and bars for them to serve. They live off their tips, and when I draw a big crowd, naturally, they comp my drinks and food. I'm getting a much more educated group of guys coming down here from California, and the word has spread about my shell game. I took a bunch of guys from UCLA for over $1,000 one weekend. I didn't think anything about it until a couple of days later, this rough and tough guy caught me at the pool one day and kept holding me under the water until I thought I was going to pass out. He told me I had better return the $1,000 if I knew what was good for me, so I gave it back. One of the bartenders who understands English pretty good told me the same group of students were planning to beat me up the night before they were scheduled to check out. That's tomorrow night, if I have my dates right."

"Well, you're coming with us tonight. Get your possessions. Are you going to continue working here at El Colonial? I wouldn't advise it, Walter. Take only your possessions and leave the white suit," I said like a trusting father.

When Walter returned, he was wearing Mexican farmworker, draw-string peon pants, and a pullover shirt. He looked like he had just returned from the fields after a hard day's work.

"Talk about a disguise, Walter. I wouldn't recognize you in that getup," said Patrick. "All except for the shoes—those are about a year's salary to '*Juan*' the plantation worker."

"They're mine. I had 'em made to fit my big feet," said Walter.

"Gentlemen," said Walter, "I will meet you in the parking lot at the front of the building. Not even my friends and fellow workers here at the hotel would allow me to walk through the lobby to the *porte cochère* dressed in these clothes."

Walter arrived with one small piece of luggage, not one of the pieces we had brought to Mexico on the SS Caprice. He also carried a large navy duffle bag filled to breaking point.

"What do you think Señor Gomez is going to say when he finds out you are no longer working for him?" asked Patrick.

"Probably relieved that I am gone," said Walter. "He couldn't pay me under Mexican labor laws, and I'm sure he had already heard about the UCLA guys threatening to beat me up. He was a good guy."

The cab ride was bumpy as we traveled up hills and into dark valleys, but both Patrick and I felt confident as Walter gave instructions to the young driver.

I signed the register at the Fairmont, presented the cashier's check for one month's payment in advance for the room, and asked both Patrick and Walter to also sign the register.

"There will be no skipping out on any hotel bills from now on. Do you both understand? No sudden 'French Leave,' and no 'pea under the shell' games either. Your room is paid for the next 30 days, and just so you know, Walter, I am about to give Patrick his $10,000 pesos from his agent, Mr. Edmunds. That's about $830 US dollars for essentials, like food for both of you. What you two do about the drink part is between the two of you. I have airline reservations back to Los Angeles next Friday. Until then, every night I intend to rotate with Walter between the other double bed and the sofa in your room. Having lived with you for so many years, Walter, now is the time to empty your pockets, duffle bag, suitcase, and any secret slot in your expensive sandals to pull out any form of money you have. It's going in the pot, so to speak, and neither of you have a pot to piss in."

"Well, I don't know about you two, but I'm famished Those shrimp things were tasty, but ever so small," complained Patrick. "Let's head out to a nice restaurant, have a couple of drinks, and a good thick steak. I could eat a horse."

"I have a better idea, Patrick. How about room service, three club sandwiches, three bottles of distilled water? I'll pay and call it a meal. All this going out to expensive restaurants and soon you'll be swiping food off the trays in the hallway from other guests who ordered room service."

"See, Walter, I told you that I could get Raub to pick up the tab for dinner tonight, didn't I? Order away, oh Money Master. You remind me of one of my characters in my book *Genius*. The income tax collector—always after the money and where it is coming from. I'm the central character, totally in control of everyone, cash poor with countless ex-wives hounding me, the world's greatest theatrical producer. Although, some of the productions are questionable. I'm pompous to the point of making an ass out of myself. Patrick Dennis is the protagonist and tells the story. Walter, here, could be the fool selling the winning Mexican Lottery ticket in his present peon attire."

Walter lit a cigarette and turned to Patrick. "I don't know if I really want to be in your book, Patrick. I still haven't forgiven you for leaving me drunk, spread out on the floor of that apartment down near the docks. When I finally woke, I had been robbed of everything, my wallet, identification, college ring, and even my shoes. I was terribly sick and still drunk. I had fouled my clothes to the point nobody would get close to me. You were nowhere to be found. I waited in the apartment until the owner came and called the police. I spent two nights in jail until they found the creep who stole my wallet and identification. That's when the cops let me go. I gave them the address of the house at the top of the hill, *Cumbre de la Montaña* as the place that you and I were supposed to be living. I don't know why, but they believed me and even drove me all the way up the hill. That's when I figured I had to slow down on my drinking. The Mexican lady who was hired to keep the house clean fed me and got me to the point that I could keep food down. Her son worked as a bartender at El Colonial Hotel, and he introduced me to Señor Gomez, the General Manager. These Mexican peon pants belonged to her husband. I had nothing and nobody."

There was a silence among the three of us until I spoke. "I've changed my mind, Patrick. I will take both of you out to a fine restaurant. Walter, in those plastic bags that Patrick has been safeguarding, do you have anything that you can wear? It doesn't have to be high fashion but do get out of that peon outfit!"

Walter showered. He seemed happy with what was left of his clothes. I decided to talk to the illustrious humorist Patrick Dennis. Not to hear plans of his forthcoming novel, but what his intentions were as far as taking better care of Walter once I returned to Seattle.

"I must say, Patrick, that I find your attitude toward Walter to be despicable and disgusting. Do you ever think of anyone except yourself? How could you wander off leaving the poor kid flat on his stomach in his own vomit and never come back to assist him? Leaving him in that state is offensive and contemptible. I still haven't given you your $10,000 pesos from your publisher. Maybe I should give the money to Walter and let him dole out the pittance each time you want a pack of cigarettes or a drink. The decision of what I do with the money is totally up to me."

I waited for my temper to settle down. Patrick cleaned himself up, changed his clothes, and gathered his wits about him. Then the three of us went to the pool bar and ordered drinks.

"I'm sorry, Raub," confessed Patrick. "I wasn't thinking, except about myself. I had no idea Walter could put away that much liquor. You must have had your hands full in Seattle. I couldn't do anything with him at times, and I must admit I did leave him alone in bars and to his own devices when he was drinking heavily. Somehow, he always made it home, though broke. And one time his pockets were loaded with Mexican money. He had entered a tequila drinking contest at one of the hotels, and from what he remembered, he had put all the college kids under the table with his capacity for drinking. He slept it off for about an hour, and then took the two of us to a big dinner and even more drinks. Walter is like a cat—he always lands on his feet no matter how much he has been drinking. I have a pretty good tolerance for alcohol, but Walter thrives on it."

Walter sat silently as Patrick and I talked. He limited himself to only one drink for the evening and savored it until his food arrived. Finally, he raised his near-empty glass and offered a toast. "This is my last drink for the entire month. If I'm going to help Patrick in writing his books, then I'd better sober up or he will write me into one of his stories as a peon selling lottery tickets. Patrick, what is your name in this *Genius* book of yours?"

"His name is Leander Starr, and he is the "genius" in all the things that Raub could never be. He's a hustler, a bandit, a philanderer, vain and pompous. I'll pull one of my copies out so that you can read all about Leander. I know you will love him."

Chapter Twelve
Patrick and the Lucha Libre

The week flew by, with the three of us constantly laughing, eating, and almost drinking ourselves to death. Walter's mission to stop drinking for thirty days ended. It was over, but he proved he could hold himself together better than Patrick or I. I stopped lecturing them and joined in the fun of Patrick's new idea for a book.

Walter set the rules and regulations of Patrick's work time and made him stick to the set hours. Morning writing time was from 9:00 a.m. until 11:00 a.m. Other than emergencies, there were no interruptions in Patrick's two hours of intense writing. A lunchtime repast was set at noon until 2:00 p.m. Patrick was free to do whatever he wanted from 2:00 p.m. until 4:30 p.m. At that time, he did his meditations before rereading his notes and typed efforts from the morning.

Walter and I both thought Patrick would either sleep away his afternoon free time or hold court at one of the many hotel bars, but he didn't. Instead, short outbreaks of exhilaration could be heard, declaring his own genius, coming from the lanai balcony after a fury of typewriter noise.

"I have done it! The chapter is perfect! I have modified your suggestion, Raub, about the hotel. It must be a run-down dump, a former castle. Maybe I should make it a former nunnery—lots of arches and steps leading up and down like I made it in *Genius*. I called it Casa

Ximinez. It is owned by none other than Catalina Ximinez, the meanest woman in town. I didn't make her name Jiminez or 'Heminez,' as it is pronounced in Spanish. Because she is hated so much, the locals will call her 'Madame X.' My readers will read her name in print the way I want them to, Catalina Ximinez, and heavy on the 'X.' We simply have to go back to that little market near the theatre district and find that delightful shriveled up old lady who sells those detestable sugar candies. Oh, you know which one I mean, the old lady without a tooth in her head. Ah! But what a face! She is like Madame X's mother, and yes, Raub, the Ximinez car was your *Hispano Suiza* touring car. Madame X will be a long ago faded 'one-picture' Mexican movie star and has never forgotten the time she strutted her boobs as an Incan princess before Leander Starr's silent camera. But now all she has left are her sagging tits, wrinkled skin, and over cosmetically enhanced eyes and mouth. She snarls when she talks. She's sort of a Charles Laughton in drag."

We gathered in the lanai of our room and ordered cocktails and trays of tempting appetizers, shrimp, and preserved strips of beef jerky. The head chef of the Fairmont was a constant visitor to our little room, grateful for many of Patrick's food and hors d'oeuvres suggestions. The room service waiters were all our friends, and some of them visited our room to serve and wait on Patrick. Most of our food and beverage charges were mysteriously added to other tourists' bills, which failed to be noticed by anyone checking the number of drinks they ordered or even their prices.

The evening cocktail hour was special for the three of us. It was when Patrick mesmerized Walter and me, and the waiters, with what he had written that day.

Patrick was a terrible typist, and often when his mind stuck, lacking just the proper word he wanted, he would type, "_____, you know what I mean!"

Strikeovers on the portable manual typewriter, which once belonged to Roger Danbury, the Seattle attorney, resulted in some keys sticking, which exasperated Patrick. Frustrated, he forced more and more keys into a twisted, tangled mess. Finally, a hotel maintenance man, aided by a pair of needle-nose pliers, succeeded in realigning the forty-eight keys.

Once again, they struck the paper in the correct spot and did not become entangled due to Patrick's fury of finger and fist punching.

My official duty was to transcribe the hundreds of scraps of paper to his main story pages. A small note would read, "Put this in at #46," but the note was blank, or he had written something on a piece of toilet paper using his liquid ink fountain pen. When I questioned Patrick, he became annoyed at my disruption of his thoughts and said, "You ass, I haven't figured out yet what I want to say at point #46. Just leave a big blank space, and I'll do it later. Now leave me alone!"

Sometimes he was kind in his requests for assistance. "Raub, please read me the third paragraph. I want to hear how the average reader is going to interpret my glorious words."

"Average reader, indeed," I would complain. Patrick could barely type, and he had no use for the rules of spelling. He precisely knew the word he wanted to use, and spelling it correctly was immaterial and laborious to him at best.

To perform my contribution to his "comic novel that was about to set the *New York Times* Best-Seller List on fire" required organizing thousands of small notes and loose scraps of paper. I asked at the hotel main desk where I could buy a typewriter to complete my share of the work. The back-office manager, who had enjoyed several of Patrick's readings on our lanai, said he would take care of the situation. The office manager was very good-looking and carried an "air" about him that reminded Patrick of another character from his book *Little Me*. "It is a comic novel told by the use of thousands and thousands of photographs. The protagonist is Belle Poitrine. Isn't that a divine name? Poi-treen. In a way it's very Southern sounding, don't you think? But she really isn't, in my book. One of her young lovers is Letch Feeley. Now, the next time you see Armando coming up here for a drink and some more of my hilarious recitation, look him straight in those beautiful dark eyes, and think 'Letch Feeley' Ooh! I've got hundreds of names for everybody. Also, you two may have observed that my Spanish is rather 'hit or miss," and Armando has consented to read my drafts to add the proper local Spanish. I'm after color, not grammatical Spanish, *comprender?*

Walter and I suspected that a little more than Spanish translation classes were taking place in Patrick's room when a large cardboard box containing a new IBM Electric Typewriter arrived. It was from Armando, né Letch Feeley, with his compliments. Unfortunately, it was also noted that an unlicensed repair shop would have to do any future repairs—the typewriter's serial number had mysteriously been filed off. The box also contained four unopened reams of thin paper.

Patrick was ecstatic over the thin paper. He found that a trusty #2 lead pencil produced more flowing, understandable lines for me to translate rather than the hundreds of small scraps of paper.

"But I haven't even had my coffee this morning and you expect me to sit at that damn typewriter and create—well, you're as crazy as Walter is. I shall return to my bed and hope that the muse of creativity casts her frivolity in my direction."

"And what happened to all that 'creativity' you spouted last night when you had that group of tourists in stitches, recalling your battle with the African pygmies?" Walter asked.

"You know perfectly well that I have used that story line before. I think I either wrote it somewhere or told somebody about it. Maybe I could change it around slightly and make it part of yet another story. Raub, that's a good idea, Raub. Be a sweetheart and bring me a cup of coffee; would you? I want to get this down before it escapes right out of my head. In fact, that's where my *Genius* story began, in Africa. It was the Edward Hotel in Durban, the hustle and bustle of the period just after the war. I'm going to need more paper. Do trot down to the front desk and tell them some story, like you're a schoolteacher, and you are about to write to your students about what a wonderful place Mexico is—and especially the Fairmont Acapulco Princess. Oh, you'll think of something, but do hurry, dear boy. Yes, I love using international cities. *Genius* started in Africa, and then a romp in my favorite city, New York City. I had Patrick as the narrator, a refined family gentleman of wit and knowledge, an advertising executive. I had another brilliant idea. I put Louise, my wife, in it as well. Oh, the kids were shuffled off to a boarding school while the parents lived in Mexico City each year, writing hysterical magazine article after article, sort of a Noel Coward and

Gertrude Stein combination. Oh! It was wonderful, full of dazzling characters."

The day before my scheduled Friday departure back to Seattle, Patrick decided he wanted the three of us to attend a *Lucha Libre.*

"What in the hell do you want to attend a wrestling match for?" Walter demanded.

"Not just a common old wrestling match, but a *Mini-Estrella.* The Mexican people simply adore their midgets. They're not dwarves, you know, and they're about the same size as my pygmies were in Africa. I really must see them, and there just so happens to be a show this afternoon near the *bahia.* The locals have given each of them names. They call them their pets or *mascotas.* Armando has lent me his camera. Walter, you will oversee taking pictures, while Raub and I will make copious notes of the expressions and appearances of these replacements for my African pygmies."

Patrick's constant prattle in the taxicab had me a little on edge. He spoke as if he were wired or high on marijuana.

"What is with you, Patrick? We are only two blocks from the hotel, and you have talked on six different subjects—from the current exchange rate of the American dollar to Armando's sore throat. You've also displayed a heartfelt concern for my leaving tomorrow morning and commented on the quality and craftsmanship of Walter's photographic efforts to date. Now you are dead set on exhibiting your sincerest desire to be outlandish in that outrageous wardrobe! Why are you wearing a black opera cape, and where did you ever find it in the first place? Did you steal it from Velos, or was it Yolanda when we were on the SS Caprice? When I saw you stepping out of the elevator at the hotel, dressed like Adolphe Menjou about to do a scene with Marlene Dietrich in the film, *Morocco,* I nearly fell over. And furthermore, Patrick, what *is* that patch of orangey-brown stuff pasted to your upper lip? Have you been trimming your pubic hairs again? I must admit, you do fill out the front of your Scottish kilt rather well. Are you harboring a concealed weapon down there, or is that your sporran purse under your Highlander skirt filled with your loose Mexican coins."

"Oh, enough of your sordid sarcasm, Raub. You will see once we reach the arena, the crowds will go simply mad over my attire."

"You aren't really considering entering the wrestling ring, are you? You do realize that all *luchadores* are required to wear a mask, hiding their facial features, and that small patch of peach fuzz on your lip doesn't qualify. I've seen some of these matches on television. You would probably be entered in the middleweight category. Some of those guys weigh up to 250 pounds of stark bristling muscle. I take that back, now I know what category you will be wrestling in. It will be *El Exótico,* as a gay character in drag. For God's sake, man, we're going to a sports arena, not a costume party thrown by Pearl Mesta. The Mexican locals will eat you alive over the curiosity of your wardrobe."

"Oh, do be still, Raub. If I had wanted to be an *El Exótico,* I would have worn a dress. Now, pay the taxi man, and let's be off."

Chapter Thirteen

The Mexican Wrestling Match and Enano – El Mini-Estrella Excelente

I've never seen such absolute chaos in all my life. At least two of Houston's Astrodomes, including their parking lots, could fit inside this behemoth of a building. It would take a pair of high-magnification binoculars to find the catwalks suspended from the ceiling. Also, the crew of technicians who worked the klieg lights pin-pointed every wrestling arena.

I counted five wrestling arena rings as my eyes adjusted to the harsh carbon-arc lighting. The largest and the highest above the stadium floor was in the auditorium's center. Four lesser rings flanked the main-event ring. All five rings had multiple wrestlers, leaping, prostrating themselves, pinning each other to the canvas mat, or pushing and shoving their opponents, eventually obtaining a win.

Each arena had its own spotlights blazing brilliantly over the wrestlers or *luchadores*. The main arena had four wrestlers in defensive poses trying to intimidate their opponents.

Two *rudos*, the tough guys, who failed to follow the rules, were attacking the two *technicos*, or the good guys. In the ring, the *rudos* enjoyed as big a following as the *technicos*. They used any violations of the wrestling rules they could. They kicked their opponents and beat them about the head and face, while the *technicos* demonstrated a more formal combat style. Very similar to the established, more athletic, ancient form of Greco-Roman wrestling and martial arts.

I thought that all the action would take place only in the five arena rings, but pushing, shoving, fistfights, yelling, screaming insults, as well as words of love and devotion, were all around us as devoted fans hindered us from finding our seats. Long, low wooden benches, able to seat eight people, had painted numbers where you placed your butt. Whether you were fat or thin, the fourteen inches of painted, heavily worn wood was yours—no matter if your next-door seatmate weighed 300 pounds.

Patrick's costume fit in perfectly with some of those worn by the wrestlers in the arenas, as well as those wrestlers circulating throughout the massive crowd of loyal, screaming fans.

Luchadores in the cruiserweight division of around 220 lbs. were often the most popular wrestlers in the *Lucha libre*. They execute extraordinary, high-flying attacks by using the ropes to catapult themselves toward their opponents. Where they deliver a rapid-fire succession of hammering blows to the opponent's body and then apply complex submission holds.

Tag teams of three men on each side fought for a successful fall by pinning down the captain of the opposing team or both other team members. Excessive punishment is a standard referee call during these matches. When a wrestler is pushed to being pinned, he can roll out of the ring under the ropes and be replaced by a teammate of greater strength or endurance. All the wrestlers wear decorative masks, *mascaras*, or hoods, signifying whether they belong to the *rudos* or the *technicos*.

A Mexican boy put his hands on his hips and wiggled his derrière in a suggestive motion and puckered up his lips as in a kiss, and yelled, "*Faldas escocesa!*" or "Scotswoman's skirt!" The boy rushed Patrick, so Walter shoved him backward with a clenched fist. "No *exótico*—Scotsman, *escoceses!*"

A band of trumpet players played—the noise was deafening. One *rudos* wrestler was maskless, and his head had been shaved, a sign that he had lost a wager match. Given the importance of masks in Mexican wrestling, losing one to an opponent is the ultimate insult. In these fierce battles called *luchas de apuestas* or matches with wagers, the wrestlers wager their mask or hair. Putting one's mask on the line or losing one's hair against a hated opponent is a tradition in *lucha libre*, where heated feuds between wrestlers may fester for years.

Thousands of pesos are bet on every match. The unmasked *rudo* would rather suffer the humiliation of showing his face to his public and having his head shaved than live with the shame of not honoring his bets.

"Walter, please ask that old woman when the mini-mascotas make their appearance. I hope we don't have to change seats to be in front of one of the other arenas," said Patrick.

Looking for food scraps, a large dog ran loose in the wooden benches that served as seats. Children ran back and forth screaming at each other and were yelled at equally by annoyed, ardent wrestling fans. A variety of foods were being offered for sale by fat men carrying large wooden trays strapped around their necks. The trays were filthy, with tacos and other Mexican dishes. A plastic bucket held hot, steaming refried beans with a tin can for a ladle. Dubious pieces of cooked meat and greasy Mexican sausages were piled high, almost overflowing the newspaper-covered trays. Reddish oil dripped from the trays and left a trail on the debris-covered concrete floor. Dogs and rats scampered to get a share of the spillage before being kicked by angry wrestling fans.

Everyone was smoking, and a thick haze hung like a storm cloud. A mariachi band played an off-pitch version of "*Cielito Lindo.*"

A woman and a man—at least we all thought they were—stood behind our bench seats and began speaking in machine-gun Spanish to Patrick. Both were wearing bright pink tights and white ruffled blouses like Desi Arnaz, who often appeared before his Cuban orchestra, playing his conga drums.

The "man" was a very tall woman with close-cut hair and a phony black mustache that made Patrick's orangey attempt at Adolphe Menjou look pale by comparison. She was athletic in stature, with large hands and feet. The crotch area of her pink tights was more than amply stuffed with a bulging phallus of monumental proportions. The man dressed as a woman wasn't as convincing as the woman dressed as a man. He was comical with his oversized, bouncing boobs. His blonde Jayne Mansfield wig sat slightly askew on his thin head, and his lips had been smeared, or spray painted, with a deep blood-red gloss like those of a clown in the circus. Long sprigs of black chest hair poked through the fabric of the blouse, up to his neckline, which had been shaved, leaving a perfect ring around his neck.

"Walter, what is this tall masculine creature yelling at me? What have I done wrong? And should all of us be running for the exit?" Patrick screamed.

"She, he... 'it' is under the impression that you are the replacement as the third member in their *exótico* tag team. They want you to wrestle with them against three *technicos*. If you look over to the arena on the right, you will see them. They're the three midgets dressed as ballerinas. Look! They're even wearing toe-shoes!" laughed Walter. "Here's your chance to study midgets up close, Patrick. If you bend over, your head might be on the same level as theirs. I think your woman/man *rudos* is wearing brass knuckles on one hand. Come to think of it, the team she wants you to fight is sort of cute with those real round, bald heads, and bowed legs."

"Do be quiet, Walter. I must have a moment to think."

The woman dressed in the man's tights stepped forward and deftly extended a long finger under the front of Patrick's kilt. In a flash, she and her partner were able to "inspect the goods," so to speak.

Patrick's sporran swung back and forth over his blue, stretch bathing suit, which he was using as underwear. The hairy pouch with the brass clasp was filled with his booty of Mexican coins. The woman stepped backward and said to her blond wigged companion, "*Ay caramba! Es pene gigantesco!*"

"What did she say, Walter?" Patrick yelled as he slapped her finger inches away from his sporran.

"*Ay caramba* is a minced oath, but the word *caramba* comes from the Spanish word *carajo*, and it means male genitalia in slang. She thinks your pesos are your 'dingus,' Patrick! Want to drop your bathing suit and give her a good "look-see"?

"For God's sake, tell her I'm not an *exótico*, you stupid shit, or I'll tell her in my best Spanish that you want to go to bed with her! Now get them away from me!"

Then, the strangest little man I ever laid eyes on approached Patrick and bowed. His name was Al Ben Jahiz Lamas, and he was a midget, standing slightly over four feet tall. A young Mexican boy towered over him and appeared to be his assistant. He anticipated every move that Señor Lamas made. His body was perfectly proportioned, except it was two-thirds the size of Patrick, Walter, or me.

Al Ben Jahiz was dressed in a blue leotard with a floor-length white silk cape. He removed the black and white mask. The eye openings were large arrow points, and the mask flattened his ears against his head to protect against other wrestlers grabbing them, attempting to pin him to a mat. There was no opening for either his nose or mouth, only a black mesh material to aid in his breathing. The entire mask/hood extended down to his chest level when worn. He stood before Patrick, the rolled-up mask in his hand, along with his Roman baton. "You are Patrick Dennis, the writer of Auntie Mame. Is that not correct?"

"Yes, I am, and you are Al Jahiz Lamas, the poet? I am most sincerely honored to meet you, Majestuoso Herculeo!" burst out Patrick in genuine admiration.

"But I insist that you call me Al Jahiz," he replied. "My wrestling name is Enano, El Majestuoso Hercule, and my fans allow me to appear before them without my mask, so that all may see that I am indeed a man and not a teenage boy like Roberto, my assistant. Roberto is my lover, assistant, aide, and the love of my life above all others. We have been together for the last five years. At one time we were both the same height but look at my giant now!" He yelled over the noise of the five wrestling arenas that were in full competition and being enjoyed by a mob of screaming fans. "It was Roberto who persuaded me to relinquish my Moroccan stones and become his lover. Is he not handsome? My sweet

Niño con pene gigantesco? He will show you his *pene*, if you wish, but do not even imagine the mere thought that you may sample of my love, for I will challenge and fight you to the death for Roberto."

Al Jahiz had lived in Mexico for the last twenty-five years and had only entered the wrestling arena as a luchador five years ago. He was now forty years old and had enjoyed a brilliant career in Iraq and Paris as a renowned poet.

Al Jahiz was born in Basra, a port in southeast Iraq on the Shatt-al-Arab, where the Tigris and Euphrates Rivers flow into the Persian Gulf, as was his honored ninth-century relative with the same name, or at least his nom de plume, Al Jahiz. The full name of his illustrious ancestor was Abu Uthman Amr ibn Bahr al-kinnani al-fuqaimi al-Basri, the poet and writer. His earlier ancestors came from Morocco.

"How did you find me, Señor Dennis?" asked Al Jahiz.

"I was searching the *Gufa Telefonica de Acapulco* for interesting names and found the listing of Abu Uthman Amr ibn Bahr. I knew he died a longtime ago, so I called you, but I was most surprised when you answered the phone with 'Al-Jahiz.' Then I knew I had made contact with someone of importance. Thank you for accepting my stupid telephone call and inviting me here today. I am honored. Walter, Raub, this man is the direct descendant of Al-Jahiz, which, by the way, means 'boggle-eyes.' Señor Lamas, please show my friends your eyes so that they may see that you were properly named."

"I am happy to meet your friends, and I hope that they research my illustrious ancestor of his triumphs in literature. He was more than a poet, but a visionary of the future as well. Although he was not a scientific man, he was the first Muslim to develop a theory of evolution. Now, this all happened in the year 908 AD, and became a major part of Charles Darwin's beliefs. Then he wrote a book about misers, which is still reprinted in magazines throughout the Arabic-speaking world even today. His finest book was on the Zanj, or Black Africans. He was able to highlight and promote the outstanding achievements of Black people in all religions and influence anywhere in the world due to the environment that made them so successful. It is his finest work and holds true even today," boasted Al Jahiz.

"You made mention of Roberto asking you to remove the Moroccan stones. I would guess that is a load off your mind," giggled Patrick.

"Oh, Señor Dennis, you are a wit, aren't you?"

"Walter, Raub, allow me to explain. A Moroccan man's hair should always be short and neat. Long, messy or beatnik hairstyles are often sneered at and are known as *M'shekek,* a word meaning that the wearer will never obtain a proper job or be respected. Facial beards have become less popular recently, ever since facial hair became the essential accessory for Islamic militants. A full beard is a religious statement, dating back to the prophet Mohammed. Simply wearing a beard in Morocco can cause suspicion by the police at roadblocks and gatherings. Mustaches are accepted, and goatee beards are now becoming quite popular in Morocco. The presence of dark hair on any part of the male's body is a testament to his manhood, but Moroccans firmly believe they must cover their bodies when out in the public areas. Free-flowing light–colored kaftans, which have no hoods to cover the head; *djellabas,* the long, loose, hooded garments with full sleeves; and the burnoose, or traditional red fez hats are now mostly worn by older men. Apart from being considered old-fashioned, these articles of clothing have the same associations with religious views as a full beard has. The younger generation has resorted to wearing such items on special occasions like weddings and festivals. Señor Dennis, you speak of Moroccan manhood, but you cannot always tell the extent of their manhood just by their dress or hair style. It is the custom for the women of Morocco to be shaven, especially in the pubic area. Underarm shaving seems to be more of an elective option. The penis determines the manhood of men in Morocco, how they use it and its size. Now I will tell you about Roberto asking me to remove my Moroccan stones. Young boys are selectively pulled from impoverished and needy families to enter into a life of a nokech or homosexuality. The boys who are selected must be of an age where they have not reached pubescence, and older males instruct them in the practice of masturbation on themselves as well as on others. As soon as the young boy's penis is able to reach erection, a leather string that has been soaked in sheep fat is tied around the foreskin of his penis and a small stone, shaped like an olive and selected for its proper weight, depending on the age of the young boy, has a hole drilled through its longer length, and a knot at the bottom of the string holds it in place."

"But Señor Jahiz, without circulation of blood throughout the foreskin, the skin will become infected and be at risk for even greater complications," said Walter.

"That is true, but the knot tied around the foreskin is a slip knot. At various intervals during the day, you will see young men performing a disgusting habit you Americans call 'scratching their balls,' when, in actuality, they are lifting the stones and placing them in an inside pocket of their kaftan to relieve the pressure of the weight of the stones, the slip knot is loosened, and circulation is restored. As the boys advance in age, the proportionate weight of the stones increases, and if a life-threatening case of gangrene doesn't convert them to Judaism, they are rewarded in their young adult life with having a most unusual appendage. When the boy reaches the proper age and has acquired definition of his muscular body, he is inspected in the penis area for development of the corona, or head, of his penis. If he possesses a thick ridge of flesh on the head, where the head and the shaft join together, he may be fitted with a soft leather harness that grips the penis head. Then the stones are removed, making urination easier. This disgustingly filthy condition does not hamper homosexuality, as Muslims do not participate in oral sex, and the leather string is untied from the penis before masturbation or engaging in anal intercourse. A further enhancement enjoyed by the gay Moroccan is that as more weight or more stones are added, the old weights are usually not removed. Additional stones are added to the leather string. It is most frightening to espy a gorgeous black-haired Moroccan in his light-colored kaftan, flashing a big smile... and then he strikes a dramatic pose with his arms raised high above his head and begins to wiggle his hips like a belly dancer. That is when the clicking and rattling of the dangling stones can be heard. "It is his offer to, as your Mae West would say, 'Come Up and See Me Sometime.' Now, gentlemen, I must leave you, as it is my time to enter the ring. I am matched against Sucio, the pig. He is evil, and I am the good one in this match, but alas, I have prevailed too long as the virtue of goodness—always winning every match—and the *funcionarios* say that I must lose this day and that it will increase the audience attendance for Sunday's performance. Sucio promises to pin me following one of his flying 'buzzard' leaps from the ropes. I will appear to be stunned as he demands the referee's confirmation that I have been pinned. I will not allow false impressions that he or anyone else is stronger than I am. I agree to acquiesce to the demands of theatrical entertainment, but not to the dishonesty of a lie."

"But Señor Jahiz, surely your fans know that you are faking your loss. If Sucio is the evil one in the ring, he must not have any fans to support him in this staged 'win,'" said Walter.

"Ah, my new young friend, he and I have the same adoring and hating fans. If you win the bout, you are loved. If you lose, you are also loved. The fans do not worry about such things. To them, it is entertainment, and the passion of the moment of triumph or defeat is the same to them and will draw them back for the next rematch. *Lucha Libre*, the *luchadores*, no matter if they are the good guys, *technicos*; or the bad guys, *rudos*. To the fans it is like your American soap operas on television: You love to love somebody, and love to hate them as well. It is theatre. I am a *mascotas*, or midget, who is a pet to millions of fans, and, besides, it pays very good money."

Al Jahiz bowed a low gesture of respect as Roberto handed him back his Roman baton. "We shall all dine together tonight at my home. I will send my car at seven this evening. We shall dine on Moroccan food and sit on cushions on the floor, so do dress comfortably. I shall attempt to explain all about midgets and pygmy tribes to you then, Patrick."

As he climbed the steps to enter the arena under the thick white ropes, he paused in recognition of his loyal fans who shouted his name, "*Enano, El Majestuoso Hercule! Enano— El Mini-Estrella Excelente!*"

Chapter Fourteen
At Last, A Touch of Elegance

The home of Roberto and Al Jahiz could best be described as eclectic. Their taste in furniture and antiquities was as diverse as they were. Significant works by Andy Warhol hung suspended above intricate Belgium needlepoint tapestries. A Chinese opium bed dominated their bedroom. Work counters in the kitchen were at two levels, one for six-foot-tall Roberto and the other twenty-six inches from the floor for Al Jahiz. Some furniture was low, more like cushions, while the balance of the living room was standard chairs and tables. Al Jahiz's massive library contained extensive French, German, English, Turkish, Iranian, and Russian collections. All four walls of the library had a moveable ladder to assist Al Jahiz in reaching the top shelf.

Al Jahiz was passionate about his collection of Peking yellow glass and his prized Japanese *Haniwa* statuary in red terracotta clay. In addition, his private study housed his vast array of Frida Kahlo and Diego Rivera works of art and memorabilia, along with years of correspondence with them worldwide.

"It was Frida who pushed my interest in Japanese clay art. She said that I reminded her of the clay warrior figures in the Tokyo National Museum, so I had to have one to see what she was talking about." Said Al Jahiz. This little painting is one of my favorites. It's by Frida. It's the house she was born in. It's called *La Casa Azul*. The house is still there in Coyoacán, just on the outskirts of Mexico City. When she died, I gave

Diego Rivera the pre-Columbian urn that her ashes were placed in. You really must see the exhibition of her works, especially her self-portraits. She and Rivera fought night and day about everything and everybody. She called him *La Centinela,* the Keeper, and he called her his *La Paloma* or Dove. Were you aware that she had a notorious affair with Leon Trotsky? Frida and Diego sheltered Trotsky and his wife in their home when they were forced to flee Russia and seek political asylum from the Stalin regime. Trotsky's wife found out about the affair and told Rivera. Rivera had a terrible temper, and he kicked Trotsky and his wife, and Frida, out of his house. Oh, he and Frida finally kissed and made up. Still, he never spoke to Trotsky again, and a few years later, Trotsky was assassinated by another Communist nut, Ramón Mercader. Trotsky was stabbed with an icepick. Mercader served twenty years in prison for the crime."

"But I thought Kahlo and Rivera were avid Communists," said Walter.

"Well, yes. You could say that about half the population of Mexico, are at least leaning in that direction. Kahlo was bisexual and had affairs with both men and women. Diego went crazy when Frida had an affair with another man, like the sculpture artist, Isamu Noguchi. It didn't seem to bother him when she had affairs with women. Josephine Baker was one of the most famous, but Frida liked a variety of wealthy and influential women: Rosamond Pinchot; Dorothy Hale, who also had an affair with Noguchi; as well as Claire Boothe Luce. Dorothy Hale jumped out of a New York City high-rise, and Frida was hired by Luce to paint a portrait of her. Unfortunately, the portrait was a little too graphic in recording the death of the troubled young girl. Frida entitled it *The Suicide of Dorothy Hale,* and Luce hated the painting so much, she had it securely crated and put in storage. Raub, this is something you might be interested in. It's my autographed copy of Tennessee Williams's *The Glass Menagerie.* Patrick tells me that you also know Mr. Williams."

"Yes, I met Tennessee years ago at a performance of *The Rose Tattoo* along with his friend, Frank Merlo. My friend and I also were lucky enough to meet Truman Capote as well," I replied.

"We must lunch one of these days and trade stories," Al Jahiz said with a winning smile.

Dinner and the conversation that evening were delightful, and we touched on many subjects. Al Jahiz was eager to discuss Patrick's success with *Auntie Mame*. Walter wanted to learn more about the mummies discovered in the Guanajuato caves.

I was the odd-man-out. It was my last night in Mexico with Patrick and Walter, and I was sharing them with two interesting new characters, Roberto and Al Jahiz.

"Raub, you haven't said much this evening," said Al Jahiz. "It is as if your mind is elsewhere. Patrick has told me of your departure from our city tomorrow. Are you happy to be returning to your rainy Seattle? I don't think so. You have the same look on your face that I had twenty-five years ago when I arrived in Mexico—the look of wanting to know more about this fascinating country and its people."

"My love of this country is much different from Walter's and Patrick's. Theirs is an escape at this point in their lives. I have been to Mexico numerous times and always loathe the day that I must leave and return to the reality of living elsewhere. I can leave tomorrow and be away from the Mexican people, their language, and their struggle to create a life in this land for countless years, only to return with the same fascination and love that I had in prior years. You and I, Al Jahiz, share the same emotions about Mexico. We would live here forever if we could."

"It sounds to me as if you do not want to leave tomorrow morning for Seattle. Am I correct, Raub?"

"You are perfectly correct, Al Jahiz, for it was during dinner tonight that I knew my future lay here in Mexico. Patrick and Walter are merely an excuse for my staying tomorrow, but I know my heart will always be with this country."

"Patrick, seeing me fight in the arena is not broadening your impression of this beautiful country," said Al Jahiz. "You three should get out into the countryside and discover some of our wondrous treasures being unearthed. I know you have taken hundreds of notes about my 'little people,' the midgets, and will somehow transform them into your new book. Now, get out and see Mexico, not the crowds of Acapulco or Mexico City. Go to the Guanajuato Caves and see the mummified bodies. See and live Mexico's vast history."

Patrick decided to explore more of Mexico and told the three of us that it was time to leave the "Riviera of Mexico" and explore some of the country's railroad lines. The conditions of the train compartments, and the engine, changed every hour of every day, depending on breakdowns and passenger loads. Sometimes, modern conveniences onboard were up to US standards. Other times, less so. We rode on converted cattle cars with wooden benches as seating, and no lavatory facilities. The train stopped once in the morning and once in the afternoon. Tourists, and Mexican citizens were obliged to climb down from the five-foot-high cattle car. Women made a beeline into the grasses, jungle, or sand dunes to squat and do their business. Men ducked between the cattle cars hitching mechanism to go to the other side and *orinar* on a cactus plant!

After our first Mexican railroad experience, traveling from the *Palenque* ruins in the *Chiapas District* to *Merida* in the *Yucatan Province,* we learned to fold toilet paper into pads. Then we placed them in our back pockets as additional padding and comfort against hard, splintered wood benches.

Walter became friendly with a young man whose family immigrated to Mexico from Italy over a hundred years before. Manuel Scagliotti was a student of archeology, specifically Incan and Colima histories. He was vacationing in Acapulco and offered to drive us to Oaxaca, where he was doing recovery work with an expedition from the National Autonomous University of Mexico.

Patrick was packed within an hour, and the last few copies of *Auntie Mame* were distributed into Walter's and my luggage. Our possessions had shrunk to a manageable size for traveling in the last few months. The electric typewriter from the Acapulco hotel had developed problems, so Walter took it to a pawnshop. They accepted it after they plugged it in to test it, and, for some strange reason, it worked! Patrick still had his portable typewriter, which he carried in his backpack, along with the remainder of his thin onionskin paper.

Walter had gone completely native. His tan was so dark that he could be mistaken for a peon worker. He wore simple white cotton trousers, a pull-over peasant shirt, and a workers' straw sombrero. The expensive sandals from his days at the El Colonial were gone, and cheap, open leather sandals protected his feet. A thick, leather money-belt around his waist held up the peon cotton trousers. He, as well as Patrick, had long since stopped wearing underwear or socks.

"I have everything I need in my backpack. A razor, toothbrush, bag of salt, a few Band-Aids, my other pair of pants, and a fresh shirt," Walter boasted.

Walter's hair was now braided into a black pigtail. Found pieces of white string secured the pigtail, as rubber bands were a luxury. The three of us were always on the lookout for any lying about.

I cut Patrick's hair, always mindful to trim the long strands he religiously combed over his bald spot. He returned the favor or thought he returned the favor when my hair started growing over my ears. Unfortunately, I often missed a large chunk of hair on the back of my head, or I suffered the loss of one complete sideburn.

When the scissors became too dull, we dampened our hair, smoothed it back with the one comb and brush among the three of us, and called it a day. I believe the descriptive term would be that the three of us were "earthy" in appearance.

Traveling in a luxury car was wonderful. Manuel brought food and drink for all of us. We left on a Tuesday morning from Acapulco, heading north on Highway 950 to Morelos. The road to Morelos wound back and forth and up and down for what seemed like a thousand miles of potholes, herds of sheep blocking traffic, and the peon's slow junk automobile or donkey cart in front of us. Passing slow traffic was dangerous at best, as in places where the road was only one lane. Mexicans whose automobiles were in fine running condition, or a truck driver eager to deliver his wares, paid little attention to oncoming traffic. Eventually, we joined a two-lane highway that took us directly to Oaxaca.

"Gentlemen, you will find literally hundreds of museums here in Oaxaca," said Manuel. "My university has been digging here for decades now, and we haven't even scratched the surface in recovering the vast amount of pre-Columbian art that is still buried. Tomorrow I must be present at the digging site and will be there until next Sunday evening. I am inviting you to take advantage of my house in downtown Oaxaca, where you may visit countless museums. I will then have three days to spend with the three of you in exploring this region."

Manuel's home, or *casa grande,* was exquisite and furnished with modern furniture and priceless antiquities. He employed a cook, a housekeeper, and two gardeners, of which one would act as our tour guide for the week.

Manuel's younger brother, José, was staying in the house. Soon the four of us were visiting every museum, garden, and restaurant/bar we could find. José was 18-years old, very handsome as a Mexican/Italian, and very much in love with a local girl, Alicia.

Alicia was the daughter of Manuel's cook, Basilia Cortez.

I will attempt to be kind in my description of Basilia. Patrick would be angry if I did not do justice to Basilia, his favorite. He adored her from the minute he laid eyes on her.

"Look at that nose!" he cried excitedly. "She has all the features of a true native pre-Columbian. She could be a Mayan or even from Colima. Have you ever seen such hair in all your life? She looks like Boris Karloff in drag or a shorter Marie Dressler. I don't know which. Whatever has happened to her skin and those teeth?"

Basilia probably knew her age, but she didn't want anyone to know it. She was the absolute epitome of a female monster but possessed all the love and devotion she could possibly hold within her withered body. She had a hump on her back and at one time, had suffered a stroke as she favored her left side and arm. Her salt and pepper hair had a pure white streak running from above her left eye, up and over her head. Her voice, low and raspy, was that of a miserable hag, but she spoke no ill will to anyone. She also had difficulty controlling the saliva that constantly dribbled from the corner of her mouth.

On first seeing her, children ran in the opposite direction, which made her cry and turn away, as she loved children. Alicia did all of

Basilia's shopping, as she refused to appear in public. She adored Manuel but was a prisoner in his home.

When Patrick first visited her in the kitchen, she turned away, pretending to be doing something else.

"Basilia, if I may call you by your first name, you are a wonderful cook! Please allow me to watch your preparation of tonight's meal. Alicia tells me that you are making lamb tonight. Please, Basilia, allow me to stay and watch you."

After a few more of Patrick's compliments, Basilia had him with an apron around his waist and peeling onions. She adored his fractured Spanish and lavish compliments about her cooking skills. They bonded immediately, and Patrick now had a new character for one of his books.

Basilia always made sure that Patrick received the finest cut of meat and choicest portion of fresh vegetables at the dinner table from that moment on.

Chapter Fifteen
Breakin' Up is Hard to Do

The three of us traveled all over Mexico to places that no one would ever think of visiting. We had ridden buses or walked the entire country several times. We looked like three homeless bums standing on the corner, waiting for a local peasant bus to take us to another archeology dig or some outdoor restaurant that promised all-you-can-eat for $10 pesos. We quickly learned that "all you can eat" meant diarrhea.

Walter's dark tanned skin and shabby clothing resulted in him sometimes being denied seating at restaurants. He then resorted to guttural English to prove his ethnicity, that of being the ugly American.

Patrick was now back in the good graces of his agent and publisher and was still writing and taking pockets full of notes. Money began flowing once more into Patrick's empty coffers. Neither Walter nor I ever knew how much money Patrick had in his possession at any one time.

"I'm treating for dinner tonight. I imagine that this will bring the three of us back to being even on expenditures, won't it?" announced Patrick.

"Hardly, my dear Mr. Rockefeller. I have been running a tab on your cash outlay for the past three weeks and have even taken into account your compulsive over tipping. I calculate that you have spent about $2,450 pesos in treating the two of us. That's about 200 American dollars. You're still shy about $450 to me and almost twice that amount to Walter. But then, who's keeping score?"

Patrick stormed out of the restaurant, creating a cloud of dust with his brisk pace on the short walk back to our hotel.

Walter and I stopped at the *tabaquería* to buy cigarettes on the way back. Once back in the dismal room with only two beds, we were surprised to find Patrick fully packed with his belongings neatly stacked near the door. He sat poised for a combat of words with the two of us.

"What's up, oh Master of the Words?" Walter asked.

"I am leaving to return to Acapulco. I can no longer live this way in this impoverished condition. I hold no interest in your constant traipsing off to some ruins or archeological site. Now that I am back writing again, I wish to be surrounded by the amenities and finer things in life rather than having to make do with cheap peasant sustenance. I never want to fill my belly with Mexican beans ever again. My publisher has given me an advance on my latest book, which I wish to inform you that I have managed to write entirely on my own. It is my passport out of this hellhole and back to civilization, someplace where halfway intelligent people speak English and don't smell or look like peons."

"That must have been one hell of an advance, Patrick," said Walter.

"Enough to help me get my wits about myself and get out of this destitute state that I have been in for the past months of living with the two of you."

"Patrick, your words cut deep, as deep as the words that I spoke to you at the restaurant. You were unusually silent, not your typical running off at the mouth. So both Walter and I suspected that something was bothering you."

"I received a bundle of forwarded mail from Guadalajara via the American Embassy. Louise sent five letters. I do wish she would simply write her plea for me to come home to New York City, and not include ghastly photographs of Michael and Elizabeth. I think she poses them in their shabbiest clothing and screams at them to make them look frightened before she takes their picture. Raub, I do not miss Louise and the children, only the comforts of a civilized house with servants and decent food. I was never born to play the role of Scarlet O'Hara eating slop out of a boiling cauldron filled with chicken necks or pigs' feet. She was a determined, genteel lady, and I am a refined gentleman. I must return to a more civilized way of life, and I honestly prefer to do it alone. Sink or swim, Roger Danbury, Patrick Dennis, Virginia Rowans, Martha Dinwiddie Butterfield, or even the real *me*—Edward Everett Tanner III—is going to try it on his own."

Walter and I were stunned at his revelation.

Walter lit a cigarette, "Raub and I have been well aware of your past month of sneaking around, the telephone calls from pay phones so that we wouldn't know or hear who you were calling. Do you think that the *Banco de Mexico* wouldn't telephone the hotel to verify that you were indeed registered here when you cashed that large, certified check yesterday? I can't speak for Raub, but as for the money that you owe me from those early days in Puerto Vallarta and Acapulco, let's just call it even. You're paid up with me, Patrick. I don't need or want your lousy money. You're going to need every cent to survive alone down here in your civilized Mexico. Personally, I think you'd be better off going back to Louise and your kids. That affair you had with that military guy you met in Acapulco didn't last very long, did it? I think Raub and I are both tired of taking care of you. Just don't put me in one of your books, or I'll sue yah."

"Well, that leaves you, Raub. Do you detest me as much as Walter does?"

"Hardly, my dear. I have enough money for Walter's airfare, along with the ticket I already have, to get us back to Seattle. But I, like Walter, feel a little put upon with your decision of 'I vant to be alone' after what we both have given up in our lives to support you in yours. You have never, not once, said a thank you. And before I forget it, you don't have to worry about paying Manuel or Basilia back the money you conned out of them before we left their beautiful home. I returned the money to them before we left on this trip. Basilia cannot afford such trust in anyone, especially you, to purchase a silk mantilla for her. She told me she plans to be buried in it and trusted you with the money to buy it and send it back to her. The $500 pesos she gave you, was that what you spent that first night in the Mexican cantina? You can also forget what you owe me, Patrick. This hotel room is paid until Saturday at noon. I am sure that Walter and I will be on our way back to Seattle after treating ourselves to proper haircuts. You will obviously be gone by then. Farewell, Patrick Dennis, and as the old saying goes, 'Don't let the screen door hit you on the way out.'"

There were no hugs or handshakes when he left, only the silence between Walter and me. An exciting and amusing part of our lives had just picked up his two suitcases, slung his cloth bag over his shoulders, opened the door, and said, "See ya."

Walter stood on the small balcony perched above the entrance to the hotel for a better view of Patrick's departure. Patrick turned, looked up, and waved goodbye when he appeared below at the dirt-road entrance. Then the taxicab driver put his luggage in the trunk, and Patrick fell into the back seat. A cloud of black engine exhaust was the last we saw of Patrick Dennis, née Edward Everett Tanner III, as the cab hurried to the main thoroughfare that ran through the heart of the town.

I mixed Walter and myself a stiff drink with cheap Mexican vodka. Then I scanned the room, thinking I had dreamt all of this. That Patrick would spring up on the floor of the other side of his rumpled bed in his usual childish way. But there was no Patrick.

"At least you'll have your own bed tonight, Raub."

"What's this?" I giggled. "Guess who forgot poor old Roger Danbury's portable typewriter?"

"Patrick always said that Danbury's typewriter gave him inspiration and luck," Walter snickered. "Do you think we should try and get it back to him, wherever he was going, or leave it as a tip for the maids?"

"Walter, we are in the only hotel in town. The maid is the woman behind the desk when we checked in, and I could have written 'Marlene Dietrich' as my name in the register, and she wouldn't have known what it meant. Speaking of 'not knowing anything,' where do you think the great Alfred, Lord Dennis of the literature world, told that poor cab driver he wanted to be driven? He never remembers that the Spanish word for airport is *aeropuerto,* not *aerolito,* which means meteorite.

Come to think of it, the closest airport is about 300 kilometers to the south at San Miguel de Allende. That's over 450 miles from here on winding mountain roads. Patrick is going to have a fit, and the next bus service to get there probably isn't for another week. Poor Patrick, I'm afraid he's played his Scarlett O'Hara drama scene a few days too early, so don't get too used to sleeping alone in his bed tonight."

Walter used the shower first. The lukewarm water came from an old gas water heater that stood rusting and hidden behind the bathroom door. As Walter showered, a loud explosion of igniting gas blew the bathroom door shut with a bang. Since the bathroom had no window or fan for ventilation, rivulets of steam vapors trickled down the enameled paint on the walls. Soon the tiled floor was awash with water that disappeared down a floor drain beneath the soiled porcelain basin that hung from the wall. This basin had no draining pipe or p-trap underneath, so the wastewater fell directly into the floor drain. When washing your hands or brushing your teeth, it was best to stand with your feet far back from the basin and lean forward to avoid getting your feet wet. Both Walter and I feared toe or nail fungus. The meager supply of towels was insufficient to dam the water from touching our feet and still have a towel to dry our bodies.

Patrick taught us how to protect our feet from the grimy floor. The lid and the seat to the toilet were both broken away from the mounting hinge. Patrick's idea was to place plastic squares on the floor in a path to the bathroom door and use them as steps. The final wiping of feet was done while seated on the edge of a bed.

I was beginning to think that Patrick was right in assessing the squalid conditions we were living in, and returning to a civilized environment was the best idea.

After I finished my cold-water shower and dried myself off, I heard a familiar voice in the bedroom. It was Patrick. As we figured, he was back—tail between his legs—and, over a stiff vodka, enthralling Walter with his brief outing.

"Darling, the nearest airport seems to be thousands of miles away from this piss hole. '*Acosar,*' I asked the driver to find out how much it would cost to get me to an airport, and he had a most strange, distressing look on his face. Then I remembered the word for quantity or amount, *'contar,'* and he began pointing at his meter and slowly counting out loud. *Uno, dos, tres...*"

"Well, no wonder, Patrick. *'Acosar'* means 'to pursue,' 'to harass,' and *'contar'* doesn't mean 'amount.' You ordered him to count!" Walter said with great exasperation.

"How many thousands of times have you heard either Raub or I ask for the check when out eating or drinking? It is always the same, *'la cuenta.'* What you should have said is *'cuánto me lleve al aeropuerto'*... 'how much to take me to the airport?'"

"Well, he must have thought I was a certified lunatic. He turned the cab around and drove me straight back to this fleabag of a hotel. He put my suitcases on the dirt walkway and sped off in a cloud of dust. He didn't even wait to be paid for the short ride."

"Señor Dennis, your bed, *'el lecho,'* awaits," said Walter. "You must try to get as much sleep as possible. The bus, the only possible form of transportation, will be crammed with peons hanging out the windows. Live chickens in twig cages will vie for the same seat that you want. This ancient, dilapidated conveyance of back-breaking transportation leaves in front of this very hotel tomorrow morning at 6:00 a.m. Don't even bother to open your suitcases or change your clothing. Between the chicken poop, dust, dirt, and sweat of the *pulque*-puking *campesino*—peasant—who will be sleeping on your shoulder, you will be as rustic as the rest of us when we arrive in San Miguel de Allende."

I didn't warm to Patrick's return as much as Walter did. In near silence, the three of us lay on top of our crumpled sheets, fully dressed for tomorrow's adventure, possibly our last together as the *trio de amigos*.

We finally fell asleep in the darkness of the stifling-hot bedroom with its screenless open windows. Then at two-thirty in the morning, I awoke to find Walter feverishly explaining to a pistol-toting policeman and the hotel's owner why Patrick neglected to pay the taxicab driver. Unfortunately, neither the policeman nor the hotel owner was in the mood to believe Walter's story of Patrick being an *estúpido Americano* at this time of night.

Then Patrick unbuttoned his flowing white dress shirt, revealing something neither Walter nor I had ever seen before. A money belt. "Walter, what does the idiot cab driver claim that I owe him, and give the figure to me in good, old, American money."

When cashing the advance check from his publisher, Patrick converted the money back into US currency. This was foolish as the exchange rate was far less in value than when he cashed the check in pesos. "Raub, the smallest, honest American money I have is a twenty-dollar bill. I refuse to pay that man four times the amount he is demanding for that short, bumpy ride in his filthy taxicab! Do be a good boy and pay him with your Mexican money, and I shall religiously reimburse you once we reach civilization."

Walter drew the hottest water he could from the leaking faucets in the bathroom to make instant coffee for the three of us. We sipped our coffee from paper cups in silence. No one spoke of the night's adventure over the taxicab driver's demands. Eventually, we descended the creaking wooden stairs to the lobby and the waiting hotel manager.

"*Señora, Señor* Dennis is most sorry for the disturbance to your fine hotel last night, and asked me to give you this, the latest book that he has written. I am sorry that it is not in Spanish, but he has signed it as the author... *autor.*" said Patrick.

The hotel manager flashed a toothless grin as she turned the copy of *The Joyous Season* in her hand suspiciously. Still, once she saw the $20-peso note between the pages, she began gushing her thanks.

"*Señor Dennis, gracias, el libro muy maravilloso.*"

"The book will be sold within an hour; you can be sure," quipped Patrick. "I rather like it, but my agent and publisher didn't."

"Oh, well," I hissed. "*Lo que sera, sera.*"

Chapter Sixteen
Puttin' On the Ritz

The torturous bus ride ended with the three of us bruised, legs cramped, and deprived of sleep the entire journey. Walter and I still looked like Mexican natives in our white draw-string trousers, pull-over long-sleeve shirts, and leather sandals. Our skin was the color of rich Belgium chocolate, and I, no longer trusting Patrick with a pair of scissors to cut my long unruly hair, resembled a young Leopold Stokowski gone mad.

Walter refused my offers for over a year to cut his long braid. The queue of glistening black hair hanging down his back had always been, without fail, the first thing to be washed when a bathroom or shower was available. Our meager supply of rubber bands had long gone. Instead, Walter learned the Mexican method of chewing on grass fibers and twining the strands into a coarse string length to bind the end of his thick braid.

Our few belongings tumbled to the road below from atop the bus.

"Patrick, I'm afraid that clinking sound you just heard is the final gasp of Roger Danbury's portable typewriter being smashed," I said. "You forgot it during your hasty departure from the hotel and I knew you'd want it, so I packed it in my duffle bag."

"Oh, Raub, you are so inconsiderate of other people's possessions. You should have informed me, and I would have stowed it away in my hard case luggage."

"There's nothing we can do about it now. What few pieces of clothing I had in my duffle bag was far too little to protect the instrument."

"Walter, find a taxicab driver and tell him that we desire a clothing store," said Patrick. "Not just any store, but one that sells proper English clothing, the whole works, from bowler hats to argyle socks. I intend to arrive in Acapulco in the style of a properly dressed gentleman. And you two, who seem to think I have failed to pay you back the miserly amount of money you profess that I owe you, shall be treated to proper clothing, enough to allow you to be seated on an airplane and not locked in a cage along with a pile of luggage."

Walter gave instructions to a cab driver to take them to the best store that sold *traje de la Ingles*.

At the store, Walter and I selected casual long dress pants, underwear (for the first time in months), proper shoes and socks, a dress shirt, and a lightweight jacket from the store's limited selection.

"Señor, what do you wish me to do with your old clothing?" asked the clerk.

"You may discard this pile," I said. "Señor Healy wishes his entire assortment of peasant wear to be wrapped appropriately, as he intends on taking it with him back to the United States. Any idea how His Nibs, Lord Byron, is faring in his selection of proper English clothing? Walter, ask our clerk to inform Señor Dennis that we are leaving the store in search of a barber shop."

Walter leafed through outdated Spanish magazines while I had my hair washed and cut. He decided to keep his braid, at least for the time being. In the end, we both looked quite handsome, in a bohemian sort of way.

Patrick was waiting for us in front of the clothing store and appeared rather huffy about having to wait for *us*... for a change.

If it hadn't been for his two hard-case pieces of luggage at his feet, neither of us would have recognized that the tall gentleman in the hat and dark-gray herringbone suit was, in fact, Patrick Dennis. All he needed to complete the English look was a monocle with the string buried in the breast pocket of his jacket. He held a long, slender, silver-tipped, black walking cane in his light-gray gloved hands. His patterned vest covered what was probably the only white, pure linen shirt, complete with an ascot tie, in all of San Miguel de Allende.

"My God, Patrick, you look like Lord Beaverbrook about to address Parliament, or in your case, would it be the House of Commons or the House of Lords?" I quipped.

"How droll you are, Robert. Actually, more déclassé. Now, have either of you two University of East Overshoe, Maine, tourists determined exactly where the *aeropuerto* office is located that will get me back to Acapulco and civilization? And before I forget, I wish to report that I have discharged the monetary obligation I owed you in exchange for your uninteresting selection of clothing. Now, if you would inquire as to the direction of the airline office, I wish to proceed, but please walk behind me. Robert, since Walter seems to have some sort of wrapped bundle in his hands, would you be ever so kind to bring my two pieces of luggage along?"

And with that, Lord Beaverbrook and his two trailing servants were off.

San Miguel de Allende is a popular city, historic and quaint to the aging "colonials" or foreign visitors who found this mountain resort years ago and have succeeded in keeping its whereabouts a secret. The few American tourists on the cobblestone sidewalks stepped to the side as Patrick approached them with his silver-tipped cane swinging dangerously in the air as a warning. "Good afternoon, Madam," he said in his best upper-class British. "Could you direct us to the Mexican National Service Airlines office?"

The American tourist grasped her startled husband's arm and executed a curtsy to Patrick. "Henry! Bow!" she shrieked. "This man has got to be the Ambassador from Great Britain or someone else very important!"

"The airport office is across the street there. Ya can't miss it, but it ain't open," the man said.

"Then if you would direct us to a refined hostelry where we may relax, and one of my able assistants can use a *teléfono* to make our necessary travel arrangements, I would be most appreciative."

"Ain't gonna' be nobody there tah take yer call. Aeromexico and Mexicana Airlines don't fly intah San Miguel de Allende. 'Bout the only way outta here is the local bus or the train outta Leon. Ain't much of a train though, bein' a freight train, and mosta' the time it ain't got no passenger car. My husband and I have been coming here for years now and love it, just the way it is, not overrun with tourists like some of the other cities. Where exactly did you want to go?" the wife asked.

"It is my desire, Madam, to reach Acapulco in as convenient and dignified manner as possible."

"Well, that's way down south, about 300 miles outta Mexico City. Yer gonna' have tah git to Mexico City tah git anywhere else in Mexico. Once the airline office opens, you can ask them the best way to git outta San Miguel de Allende and then on tah Acapulco. One year we did the local bus tah get here. Never again. I swear, somebody brought a goat along in the backa the bus. It took forever tah git here," added the husband.

The majestic Casa de Sierra Nevada Hotel came into view as we rounded the corner.

"I don't know about you gentlemen, but that is where I am staying, at least for the night, a good hot bath, cocktails, a dinner befitting the *gourmand* that I am, and a peaceful night's rest—alone in my own private room. I'm sure they have students' rates to accommodate you. Raub, give my luggage to the porter. I shall contact the both of you later, after I have refreshed myself properly."

Walter and I compared our monies and requested a double room next-door to the elegantly dressed Edward Everett Tanner III.

There was no telephone call from Patrick that evening. We waited for an invite to either his room or ours for cocktails, but no invitation came.

"Patrick's back in his element here at San Miguel de Allende. Did you see all those well-heeled people in the lobby? I'll bet two-to-one that he's mesmerizing some rich old lady in the cocktail lounge right now," suggested Walter.

"I'm exhausted from that horrible bus ride. What say we find a nice little restaurant nearby, have a couple of drinks, and call it a night?"

The food was excellent, and Walter and I reviewed all that had been happening to our little "trio." Neither of us said it, but we thought that this was possibly the last time we would see Patrick. The walk back to the hotel was enjoyable in the cool evening breeze. Walter stopped at the hotel's *tabaquería* for American cigarettes. He learned that an 'English' gentleman had purchased the entire supply of Marlboros. I checked at the front desk for any messages that Patrick may have left for us, but there were none.

The cocktail lounge was crowded with a large party of well-dressed vacationers and elegantly dressed Mexican citizens being entertained by Patrick Dennis, the highly acclaimed author of countless books. As we passed the open doorway into the lounge, laughter erupted as Patrick concluded his pygmy tribe story with a flourish of his hands in the air.

"Do you still have the solid-gold medal the African tribe leader gave you for your saving his daughter?" a tourist asked.

"Unfortunately," said Patrick, "I had to sell it to a wealthy diamond merchant in Durbin, to secure my release from the German sympathetic African warlords who were holding me captive. I barely escaped with my life."

Walter, irked at Patrick's behavior toward us, yelled out. "Hey, Patrick! Tell 'em about Señorita Estancia in Acapulco, or about your good friend Roger Danbury."

Not missing a beat with his captive audience, Patrick waved in our direction and informed the crowd that we were his hired traveling assistant and translator during his yearlong Mexican travels, searching out rare archaeological digs and indigenous native tribes for an upcoming book.

"Sort of Al Capone in Wonderland," I whispered to Walter as we went to our room.

"How about I crawl over the railing from our balcony to his and short sheet his bed? Pygmy tribe indeed," said Walter in disgust.

It was a toss-and-turn night for us, and we awoke early. It was Sunday. Church bells began their peals from the domed monastery next to our hotel.

"His Nibs isn't going to like that. We'd better order up some coffee and be ready for him to burst into our room retelling his last night's adventures without us."

The coffee arrived, and we waited, but there was no Patrick Dennis.

"Señor Dennis has checked out," the desk clerk reported.

"Did he leave any messages for either Señor Healy or me?" I asked.

"No, no messages, but he did ask that I give Señor Karr this portable typewriter. He said that he had no further use of it."

I asked how Señor Dennis could possibly leave San Miguel de Allende at this time of the morning since there was only the local bus service to Leon. Walter and I knew that Patrick would never again ride on such peasant transportation as a bus.

"Señor Dennis is traveling with Lady Whittington in her limousine. She is driving him the entire distance to Acapulco. Her staff and luggage are following in other automobiles."

"So, it's Lady Whittington now, is it?" I said to Walter. "I have no idea how much the advance from his publisher was, but since he left the last three copies of his books for me to carry in my duffle bag, he won't have the money from selling them. With his gift of gab, he could start a lecture series. His first subject could be how to defend yourself in the wrestling ring fighting off midgets while wearing a *mascara* over his face."

During the next few days of riding the local buses to Leon and then on to Mexico City Walter suggested we extend our stay in Mexico. "Let's take another bus ride to Acapulco to see how the 'World's Greatest Author' is doing without us, especially me, his interpreter. Acapulco is a popular airport destination, and we can leave Mexico from there."

The bus ride from Leon to Mexico City took most of the day, with the numerous stops to load or unload other impoverished passengers. Walter spent most of his time entertaining three small shoeless children with his pea-under-the-shell game as their concerned *abuela* looked on.

"I wouldn't get too close to the littlest one if I were you, Walter. The way he keeps scratching his head, I think he has lice."

Walter wanted to stay near the central bus station, but I didn't like the neighborhood and the beggars on the streets. "No, I will treat for the El Colonial in the District Federal," I said. "We will each have a good hot shower and a filling dinner, plenty of sleep, and then back again on that torturous bus with the loose springs in the seat."

After checking into the El Colonial Hotel, we treated ourselves to a taxicab ride to the American Embassy to check for messages or even possibly a note from Patrick. The balance of my depleted checking and savings accounts in Seattle had been wire transferred to the Banco de Mexico. Walter had a short note from his older brother informing him that his father had died, and the services had been held four days previously. Walter was devastated, even though he had long ago given up caring for his alcoholic father.

"Well, that leaves only two Healy lushes on Earth. My brother and me," he confessed while at the hotel bar. "My whole family had a great propensity for putting away the booze. Mom was one of the seven surviving Korbel cousins, who sold the champagne business to Adolph Heck in 1954. Mom died of liver cancer during the war, and Dad was a pharmacist. He owned a string of drug stores but lost all of them because of his drinking. Come to think of it, he and Mom drank up about everything they ever owned. My brother is just as bad. He has a good job with the airlines, but really lives it up on the weekends."

"Tell you what, Walter. We'll both go to Acapulco, at least to see if the world's greatest author is still living high on the hog or back with Estancia in some seedy hotel on the *mercado*. I have enough money to purchase your airline ticket back to Seattle or wherever you want to go. We, my old friend, are taking a minibus to Acapulco. They say it takes about four hours to travel the 185 miles because of the hairpin turns on the road and heavy truck traffic during the daylight hours."

"What's a minibus?" Walter asked.

"About a third the size of the clunker we just rode in from Leon. It only holds ten people. The fare per person is about $130 pesos, or $11, and it doesn't make stops along the way to let farmers and laundry women off with their wares or animals."

After a good dinner, the soft, clean sheets on the beds at the El Colonial were a welcome sight. Still, before we turned off the lights, Walter called room service, requesting a pair of sharp scissors. "Yeah," he said. "Let's do it. It just doesn't feel good without my peasant pants and shirt. Cut away, oh *Majestuoso Rauberto el barber*."

Chapter Seventeen
The Three Faces of Patrick Dennis

Mexico City is enormous, bustling, and most of the time smoggy and extremely filthy. The traffic jams never stop, allowing pedestrians to cross any street without a designated crosswalk. Only in the city's beautiful parks, or in the majestic church interiors, is there a semblance of golden, blessed silence. Vendors, hawkers, children screaming, and arguing old women, produce a cacophony on the streets, in the lobby of hotels, and even in the hallway outside your room.

Few, if any, peasant-dressed citizens in farm-work clothes are seen on the street. Still, thousands of Mexicans push, shove, try to sell you something, or show their displeasure by calling you an *estúpido* for blocking their progress or movements. Mexico City is a giant metropolis, a vibrant ever-moving behemoth of people making a living while getting from point "A" to point "B."

This was my second experience of living in Mexico. The first Mexican city that I lived in was the beautiful city of Monterrey. Monterrey was nothing like I imagined Mexico to be. It was a rich, thriving city in the foothills of the Sierra Madre Oriental mountain range. It's one of Mexico's most developed cities, with the highest per capita income in the nation, and is rich in history and culture.

I lived with an American oil executive from Texas for two years, in an enormous, converted home. It had once been a Catholic church. I traveled back and forth to Houston in his private jet. At that time, I lived a life of wealth and privilege, not like living on limited resources with Patrick and Walter.

We passed through Mexico City numerous times on Walter and Patrick's quest to visit archaeological digs to inspire Patrick's stories. Between bouts of writing, Patrick tried to escape from his previous illusionary and fictive lifestyle of fame, family, and homosexuality. This was Patrick's only adventure in living on his own without servants. I was there with Patrick and Walter, going along with the craziness because I genuinely cared about the two of them.

Walter and I had been friends for years and knew each other better than we knew ourselves. He was the easier to keep out of harm's way. Most of the time, he was alert and intelligent, but after consuming a few drinks, he drifted into a state of silliness, then the loveable drunk, and finally the dead weight of a body unable to care for itself.

Patrick was a brilliant study of dos and don'ts in his dedicated line of writing. "I like this," he'd say but hated it later, ripping the pages of scrawled notes to shreds. "My mind is a total blank. I will never write anything of importance ever again," he would often say, but ten minutes later, he was fascinated with recording the actions of a rotund cook at a roadside café, who, he thought, "would be perfect in my current story," and finally, there was his constant stepping into the shadow of depression and talks of suicide.

Walter and I soon learned what topics and situations to avoid that might bring on a state of depression for Patrick that lasted hours, sometimes days at a time. Patrick detested being alone. Alone to him meant that the two of us were in the next room as he pounded the keys of Roger Danbury's portable typewriter. Following a warning of "Be quiet. I am creating," a period of silence on our part would be interrupted by Patrick yelling to see if we hadn't slipped out and gone somewhere, leaving him alone in the hotel room.

Upon entering any room, store, restaurant, or bar, Patrick "sized up" the room and its occupants, locating someone he could rely on if Walter and I had to leave. "Let's take that table over there near the heavy-set woman. She's all alone and looks like I could entertain her with one of my stories, Walter. You sit to my right. You will be Ambrose, my nephew from Connecticut, or some state distant and in the opposite direction of where the chubby little darling claims to have come from. Oh, that didn't come out the way I wanted it to, but you understand. We've done this hundreds of times before. Raub, you will be my sec-rit-tree. Your name will be Cleveland... no, that's too American. You will be Reginald, from Durbin, South Africa. That will be my lead into a good war story or something. I'll think of something, and you Walter, sit up straight and stop slouching in your chair. You may be my nephew, but you will behave yourself and show good manners for a change."

Introductions were made. We ordered, and Patrick moved to the lady's table. I was left with our food check. Patrick sent "Ambrose" to the lobby for cigarettes, and then the two of us left Patrick and Wilma Hanover giggling over a funny story about Patrick dancing with Doris Day aboard the Queen Mary.

The suicidal moods were *not* a giggling matter.

One evening, while enjoying after-dinner drinks, Patrick confessed to his prior attempts to end his life. His stories were detailed with the exact number of pills he had ingested or his sitting in the bathtub of hot water, preparing to cut his wrists. "Other than becoming sexually aroused from the warm, relaxing water, I could not fathom the idea of ending it all by first enduring the terrible pain of gashing a razor blade across my thin dexterous wrists and then sitting in my own blood-soaked water with a hard on."

The thought of a dying Edward Everett Tanner III was terrifying. We sat and listened in stunned silence.

"Well, don't you see the irony of it all? How could I ever do such a thing that would not only cause me pain, but also to those who found my lifeless, white, bloodless body. They would carefully lift my corpse from the pink-stained water, and soon determine from the size of my erection that I had been well-endowed in manhood during my lifetime. So I masturbated in the water and forgot the whole disgusting affair!"

Other times, Patrick spoke of suicide attempts before Louise, his wife, committed him in New York City. "That was over ten years ago. That time of wanting to end it all was different. My wonderful book, *Little Me*, while a success on its own, was to be presented as a Broadway play. Neil Simon tossed my book about Belle Poitrine, with those wonderful photographs by Cris Alexander, and all those enchanting characters with their voidance of sincerity, talent, puns, quips, and buffoonery out the window. He made it into a farce, not about a funny, sexy, stage-struck adventurous lady, but a platform for Sid Caesar to strut his stuff on the Broadway stage. It was a wonder that Simon failed to rewrite my story by adding a part for Imogene Coca. Five weeks after the opening, I was devastated. I had no one to confide in, and I refused to be seen in public. I was forced to hide from the hounding press. Even my closest friends deserted me. Louise and the children failed to console me in my hour of need. I emptied the medicine cabinets of anything remotely barbiturate, washed the pills down my trembling throat with glass after glass of straight vodka, and climbed into the bathtub to drown myself. I had not eaten that morning, and my body was hollow, empty. Therefore, I floated like a balloon in the water. The barbiturates or the vodka took control. I don't know which. I passed out before I could hold my head under water long enough to end it all. Louise found me, shuffled the children off to a sitter, and called for an ambulance. It is true that this was not my first attempt at taking my own life. I found that I was despondent with the responsibility of being married, and yet, at the same time, desired to engage in sexual affairs with men. I certainly never spoke of such sexual assignations with men to Louise or anyone else, but she continued her heartfelt belief that I was just different in choosing to have close friendships with obviously homosexual men. The previous attempts at taking my life were unsuccessful, even when Louise provided me with her good-natured, wholehearted efforts to understand me better and give me the privacy I so desperately needed. The Broadway play incident was my last attempt at taking my own life. I never came home from the emergency room and the pumping of my stomach. Louise had me committed to an institution for nine months. Besides pills and medications, I was subjected to electroshock therapy. That cured me of any future desirous attempts to end it all."

After that one time confessing his suicide attempts, Patrick never mentioned it again. Patrick and I had discussed suicide before, and he knew that I supported those who performed the act and took their own lives. Walter was another matter.

Patrick was an atheist and often spoke out against all religions. Louise came from a Catholic family but was raised Presbyterian. She, like Walter, had been educated through their churches to believe suicide was a sin—not dying within the "hands of God," but by "one's own hand."

Walter believed that when a friend died following an illness or a tragic accident, it was proper to say, "God needed him."

"Let's not wait until tomorrow to catch the minibus to Acapulco. Let's try to go today," Walter said. "I'm worried about Patrick. He may be in the clutches of Lady Whittington to get a free, fast ride to Acapulco, but you know how Patrick is, he'll ditch her when he's had enough."

"Patrick told me he was going to look up his old military friend he had sex with when we were here before. Al Jahiz and Roberto are here in Mexico City, so he won't be with them. Maybe you're right, Walter. Come to think of it, I'm a little concerned about Patrick as well."

The desk clerk called the minibus company, and we were on our way. The driver spoke perfect English, and there were only three other people on the four-hour ride to Acapulco—a man and wife and their five-year-old child.

The driver explained the need to use the restroom before departing on the trip, as the bus made no stops, and sanitary bathrooms between the two cities were few and far between. Unfortunately, the couple's little boy did not heed the warning. An hour out of Mexico City, we were looking for a halfway decent Pemex filling station or *cantina* to relieve the boy's bladder.

After the emergency bathroom stop, the little boy suddenly became famished, but the driver refused to stop.

"Walter, show him your shell and pea game on a vacant seat. That should take his mind off being hungry."

The two played the game for over an hour, with the little boy constantly losing. The next hour was spent with Walter teaching him how the trick was performed and the boy challenging his father to the same game.

Perched on a steep hillside facing the Pacific Ocean, Acapulco was a welcome sight. I tipped the driver, and we took a cab to a small hotel where the three of us had stayed before.

"Tomorrow we will make plans for our departure back to Seattle. That *is* where you want to go, isn't it, Walter?"

"I have no future in Seattle. I'll go as far as San Francisco and meet up with my brother. I should help in clearing up Dad's affairs. Maybe I can get a job doing personnel work again. What do you think would be the best way to track down Patrick and his lady friend?"

"If she drove him all the way from San Miguel de Allende in her limousine, then they have to be staying in the most expensive hotel in Acapulco. That, or maybe she owns a home here. Let's check the telephone book for the biggest and best ads for the big hotels. We can make calls for either Lord Patrick Dennis or Lady Whittington. Rest assured, we'll find him. Acapulco is a large city, but once the world's greatest author has hit town and spread the word of what he has written, everybody in town will know how to find him!"

We ate a light dinner that night and walked the streets to view the flood of American tourists clamoring for a good time.

"Remember, Raub, how Patrick was always talking about the Las Brisas place overlooking Acapulco Bay, the one with the secluded rooms and your own private pool right outside your patio? I'll bet you that's where he's staying."

"It's one of the very few five-star hotels in Acapulco. I wonder just how big that advance check was from his publisher."

Chapter Eighteen

"La Matanza de las Ratas" - The Killing of the Rats

I acquiesced to Walter's request that we stay at the Fairmont Hotel. "I may even set up my shell and pea game once more to make some money," said Walter. "You can't have much left. You've been paying for everything."

"I have enough, but we won't be living on the grand scale of Patrick Dennis."

After checking into the hotel, we passed the small ground-floor bar where Patrick once told his stories of African pygmies and successfully warding off the entire German army.

I don't know why it caught my eye, but a tattered, worn copy of *Auntie Mame* was still in the collection of books lining the library wall for the hotel guests to borrow and read. I thumbed through the book and found a hand-written note in the flysheet bearing the signature of Patrick Dennis. The book, at one time, had been dedicated to Monica La Rue. "With fond memories and everlasting love," it read.

"I wonder what he charged her for this then pristine copy?" quipped Walter. "I understand the 'fond memories,' but what about that 'everlasting love' business? Patrick was switch-hitting back and forth between men and women in those days. Something must have turned Miss LaRue off Patrick. She left the book here at the hotel."

Our room was better than the last time we stayed at the Fairmont Hotel. Walter found a comfortable sofa bed on the patio. Our room faced west for the afternoon sunset. Early in the day, he curled up and took a nap while I searched through the *gufa Telefonica* for a five-star hotel where Patrick might consent to stay. I narrowed my search to the *Acapulco Diamante* region and the eastern side of the *Bahia De Acapulco*. These areas were the most fashionable, with cliffside-hanging hotels facing the deep blue water. Some even had their own golf course.

On my third telephone call, I found Patrick. He was registered at the Las Brisas Acapulco Resort as Dennis Tanner III. I declined the offer to have my call transferred to his room. I hadn't decided what I was going to say to him, and anyway, I wanted Walter to contribute his two cents worth when we did talk to him. So, I called once more and asked to speak with the hotel manager.

Enrico Diaz was most accommodating in offering information regarding Señor Tanner. I told him I was a trusted old friend of his from South Africa. That I wanted to send flowers to Señor Tanner and Lady Whittington, announcing my arrival in Acapulco. Within seconds he provided me with their cottage numbers and their location of their whereabouts on the property. He also left a pass for me at the main gate for when I visited his distinguished guests.

"Lady Whittington is occupying our largest villa, the *Casa Importante* as well as two adjoining cottages for her servants. Señor Tanner has chosen a *Cabana de Aislamiento* – a small house of privacy – a considerable distance from Lady Whittington's complex. Señor Tanner does not want to disturb the Lady with his *maquina mecanograffia* when he is writing. Will you be attending the function at Lady Whittington's casa tonight?"

"It would be wonderful to surprise Señor Tanner after all these years. What is the occasion for Lady Whittington's party?"

"It is a costume party. You are to wear peasant clothing and sandals, as the party will be held outdoors so the guests may observe the *caza de las ratas*."

"Why would someone give a party for the hunting of rats?" I asked.

"It is the time of year that all the hotels join together in the eradication of the filthy vermin from the hillsides where they have been living and breeding. The rats came to our village years ago on sailing ships and now live on our fruit and vegetables. All the hotels and private residences facing the *Bahia De Acapulco* participate in the event. Our entire staff is standing by with kettles and drums to frighten the rats in their attempt to escape to a lower elevation and the shoreline of the bay. The rats are afraid of the noise and burning torches. After a few rodents have found an escape route to the water's edge, others follow. The rats are afraid of the waters in the bay. The wide sandy beaches will not protect them, and thousands and thousands of rats will enter the water. Local fishermen have been baiting the coastal waters with fish chum to lure and attract sharks from the deep ocean into our tranquil bay. When the last rat has been driven into the water and into the hungry mouth of a great shark, the festivities begin all along the *Avenida Costera Miguel Aleman*. It is a very festive event. Lady Whittington has ordered a large festival tent to be erected on the *Avenida*, complete with a dance floor. She has invited the entire register of guests here at Las Brisas as her guests for the party. As friends of Señor Tanner and Lady Whittington, you will be most welcome."

"Oh my, it does sound exciting. Of course, we will be there! Just before sunset, you say. And we are to wear peasant clothing... well, I will see what I can scrape up!" I said, trying not to laugh.

When Walter awoke, I told him about my conversation with Enrico Diaz and the invitation to Lady Whittington's party.

"Do you really think that Patrick will dress up as a native? He still has his two suitcases of clothing to select from. Also, he has the clothes he bought in San Miguel de Allende that made him look like Lord Beaverbrook."

"I have no idea, Walter, but whatever he wears tonight, it will be smashing, unusual, and attention-getting. You know Patrick," I quipped.

Choosing from Walter's remaining collection of native Mexican clothing, the two of us drank, laughed, and dressed for the party.

"Something is wrong, Raub. I think it's our haircuts. We have the proper clothing, but we look too neat."

So, we smudged our faces with cigarette ash and messed up our neatly combed hair.

Our taxicab approached the main gate into Las Brisas Acapulco. A startled guard placed his hand on his holstered firearm upon seeing two filthy-faced natives riding in a taxicab attempting to enter the hotel. I rolled down the taxicab's window and spoke to the startled guard. "*Yo soy Señor Karr y esta es me invitado. Queremos entrar, por favor.*"

Las Brisas Acapulco is built on a steep hillside. Some of the cottages and private swimming pools hang precariously to the rocks, seemingly ready to pitch cottage, pool, and occupants to their deaths at any moment. A large gathering of guests assembled in a festive tent, enjoying the local cuisine. Lady Whittington ordered that all the food be authentic, except it had all been prepared in the hotel's massive gourmet kitchen.

"There won't be any stone grindings from a mortar and pestle in our corn tortillas tonight," joked Walter. "And I bet they're grilling filet mignon rather than goat meat!"

The guests' costumes were mostly clean, ironed, white garments and a brightly colored *serape* blanket worn over one shoulder. Women wore *mamacita* dresses and flowing aprons. They clung tightly to their expensive Parisian purses. They feared being in the same tent with so many impoverished-looking people.

There were about 200 guests, but I could not find Patrick.

Walter found one of the bars and was busy amusing a teenage girl who wore a Hermes silk *mantilla* over her blond hair. She was fascinated with Walter's crude sandals and the bronze color of his skin. At least Walter and I were tanned, as a native would be from being in the sun for such a long time.

Not just one but three *mariachi* bands drifted in and out of the tent playing their lively tunes.

"*Amigos!*" shouted Walter above the noise of the crowd. "*Como sabes tocar Malagueña Salerosa?*"

"*Si, Señor,*" a young trumpet player replied.

"Good. Ask the other *mariachi* bands to join with you in playing this wonderful song for this pretty *señorita*."

As Walter stood before the assembled mariachis and bowed, a hush fell over the audience. As guitars softly strummed, Walter sang his favorite Mexican song. After a few lines in Spanish, he translated the words he sang into English. "This is a mournful song of a young man who is singing to a woman, telling her how beautiful she is. She is a wealthy *señorita* from Malaga, Spain. He sings of his love for her and how he desires to be her only man. He pleads his case to the *señorita* and points out their cultural differences in class. He is very poor, and she is wealthy. He tells her that he understands if she rejects him. He makes one final plea for her love by holding one high note for as long as his voice will last. The song ends and you, the listeners, are to determine if he has won her heart."

Walter's song ended with rapturous applause from the guests as Patrick Dennis stepped forward to grasp his hand. He was inexplicably dressed as a Dominican friar, complete with a rosary dangling from his rope belt. Being almost bald, Patrick had artfully combed the remaining hair he had into a swirl that covered his head above his ears. He was shoeless, but he wore a pair of black rayon socks. The final *pièce de résistance* was the black Gideon Bible, with the name in gold-embossed letters, and given to all hotel guests at the Las Brisas Acapulco Hotel.

"I thought you were an atheist, Patrick. Are you going to burn up and melt for your blasphemy against the church? Like a vampire when the morning sunlight strikes your white pasty skin. Or do you now have special dispensation from the Pope?"

"Oh, do shut up, Raub. When darling Elizabeth, Lady Whittington, told me of the costume party she was giving tonight, I immediately associated peasantry, poverty, and such with the piety of the church. I had no idea you had such a fine voice, Walter. You were magnificent in explaining the song." Patrick offered hurried introductions to our hostess, Lady Whittington, as the announcement was made for the *la matanza de las ratas*. "Oh, Raub, you have got to get me out of this. I agreed to this rather pushy woman's invitation and party without knowing what *ratas* were. I thought she was talking about *retar*, something about a challenge! When she explained what is going to happen, I almost threw up! First off, I do not run down hillsides and streets, especially without proper shoes protecting my delicate feet! Secondly, she made the whole story sound as though these about-to-be-eradicated rodents were the original rodential pest who had stolen passage onboard a whaling ship to get to Mexico decades ago. Sort of a reverse Roger Danbury, you might say."

"Is it the running down a hillside that frightens you, Patrick, or is it the thousands of rats floating on the surface of *Bahia De Acapulco* about to be eaten by hungry sharks that is turning your stomach? I warned you that Mexico was not a pretty bedtime story. Can't you feign a massive coronary or something?"

"If you won't help me, Raub, I am sure Walter will."

With Patrick's assistance, Walter concocted an amazing, but hardly believable, story to Lady Whittington as to why the two of them could not join them in hunting rats. Finally, disappointed, Lady Wittington climbed into a pony cart and headed down to the shark-infested bay, leaving us in the deserted tent with full bars and mountains of food.

"Patrick, why the mixture of your two names with Lady Whittington? Why are you going by Patrick Tanner? How are you going to promote your books and let people know who you really are?" Walter asked.

"My dear boy, I am no longer Patrick Dennis, Edward Everett Tanner III, or even Roger Danbury, for that matter. I am no longer a world-famous author of countless books. I no longer write for a living. I am a designer of fabulous homes for the unimaginative. I am an entrepreneur.

I now set the standards of how people should spend their silly money on homes and where they will live. Lady Whittington and I are now engaged in an exciting new venture. We buy promising estates that are sitting idle in this stagnant market in the land of the haves and the have nots. This afternoon, Elizabeth and I purchased a rather imposing estate at the entrance of the Crowne Plaza Acapulco. We practically stole it!"

"I know you received a sizeable check from your publisher, but exactly how sizeable was it for you to be able to start a business venture with Lady Rockefeller or whatever her name is?"

"Raub, she is the bank, and I am the talent in transforming this decaying twenty-room example of colonial architecture into a magical fairyland for a rich, mainland buyer. I have three months to do my conversion to pure ecstasy before the winter season starts again here in Acapulco. Naturally, we plan an explosive 'coming out' party to show off the finished property to a select group of wealthy US citizens and diamond-rich Europeans. Oh, I can hardly wait. It will be so wonderful and rewarding, not like pouring your heart out over some silly story, only to have your expectations dashed by some old stick in the mud in New York City."

"Well, Dorothy Draper, we wish you well in your partnership with Lady Whittington. Unfortunately, Walter and I are leaving this coming weekend, and I hope you will be able to find time in your busy corporate schedule for at least a final drink or two."

"Yes, yes. We will get together. I am so confident in the success of this project that I have used a portion of my remaining money to buy a darling little condominium in the center of downtown Acapulco. I did not tell Elizabeth about it. I do all the design work and supervise the workers to transform these creations into majestic opuses of mine. All she is doing is writing the checks. This will be my little 'nest egg'"

'Nest egg—how apropos,' I thought. What will happen when the mother bird flees the comfort of the nest with all her money, and Walter and I are not here to catch the little chick when he falls from the nest?

Chapter Nineteen
When In Doubt, Reinvent Yourself

We seldom saw or heard from Patrick during the remaining four days we were in Acapulco. We were at the Fairmont while Patrick splashed swimming-pool water down the hillside at the Las Brisas Acapulco.

"The private cottages are frightfully expensive, and Walter, unless you parade your naked body at the most extreme edge of your private pool and garden, no other cottage or even a walking workman, is able to see you in your 'full glory.'" I mimicked Patrick.

"Raub, how do you think Patrick is getting along remodeling that monstrous estate? His Spanish is so limited, and he'll be dealing with the local artisans and craftsmen, who probably speak very little, if any, English. If Patrick is going to make a go of this new adventure of his, he will need a translator. Maybe I should stay on and help him out."

"If I know Patrick, he will already have secured the services of the most handsome and literate young man from the throngs of Lady Whittington's hangers-on. Patrick will have sweet-talked the bedazzled young man into working for free until that day when some unsuspecting rich tourist lays out his five-million pesos for the place, only to find that it has no kitchen or roof. The whole place will be put together with a lick and a promise, or Patrick ordered an entire wall to be mirrored *–espejo –* but he said *espeso,* which means thick and dirty."

"Better yet, Raub, you remember how he always said *lavativa,* when he needed to use a lavatory. Wait until he tells his workmen that he needs a *mucho grande* enema!"

"Walter, we both know that he will survive on his own, and I get the distinct feeling that he is the one calling an end to our partnership in his writing and friendship."

That night, following a day playing tourists, Walter and I returned to the Fairmont to find Patrick seated in the lobby like an expectant barrister about to serve papers from his ponderous leather briefcase. He sat bolt upright with his thin knees close together to support the briefcase, which now served as a writing desk. Fallen scraps of paper littered the floor around his Oxford shoes. It was eighty-six degrees outside, but Patrick still wore his heavy wool, herringbone jacket, buttoned vest, and French-cuff dress shirt, complete with his signature cravat around his neck. He also wore an identical pair of black-framed spectacles from the collection of Cary Grant, née Archibald Alexander Leach. The glasses with their obviously weak, if not clear, lenses drew attention to Patrick's elongated face with his mustache and Vandyke beard. The top of his balding head glistened under the reflective floodlights in the hotel lobby.

'Thank God,' I thought. 'He's back at his writing again and stopping all this foolishness of being an interior decorator.'

"Walter! Raub! I need your help. You have no idea what that ghastly woman has done to me. She had me locked out of my cottage at Las Brisas. My fabulous clothing and possessions are in there, padlocked like a common vagabond. She claims I owe her thousands and thousands of dollars. It was she who invited me to stay at Las Brisas, and that hideous house she bought may be in the newest and most fashionable area of all Acapulco, but it is a mess of outdated plumbing and fake architectural features that will never make it in this new style and era of smooth lines and high-gloss finishes."

"Calm down, Patrick, and come up to our room. We will sort this out over a nice cooling cocktail and give you a chance to get out of that heavy, thick jacket and vest that seems to be holding your waistline in."

"I'll have you know, Raub, that this very jacket and vest combination is the latest rage in London amongst the royal family."

"Rage or not, you are cinched up like a giddy drag queen about to go on stage wearing a corset, full bra, and please take off those silly eyeglasses! They draw attention to the beads of sweat steaming down from the top of your head."

Patrick pulled a large handkerchief from his jacket pocket and mopped his brow like an errant child.

"Speaking of the top of your head, what have you applied to your bare scalp that's holding down those wisps of remaining hair over onto the top of your head?"

"Edwardo, my design assistant, has this marvelous hairspray, and he helped me position my hair to soften the baldness of the skin. It is called *Goma Brillante* here in Mexico."

"Have you looked at yourself in the mirror, Patrick? Edwardo must have used at least two cans of the spray. Not only is it holding the few stands of hair flat against your white, pasty scalp, but the stray hairs look slick and shiny."

"Patrick," Walter added, "*Goma Brillante* means shiny glue in Spanish. Let's get you into a shower. Maybe the hot water will melt some of the crap off the top of your head. I'll go down to the liquor store and buy us a bottle. I've got a feeling that it's going to be a very long night tonight."

By the time Walter returned, Patrick had used every clean, dry towel in the bathroom, used my nail clippers to remove overgrown toenails, and was now wrapped in a hotel terrycloth robe. "I am delighted that you have returned, Walter. Yes, pour me a good one. I have much to tell you regarding the wealthy, untalented, Lady Whittington. First, let me state that she has been married four times, and not one of her husbands was a Lord, so she really isn't a Lady, is she? The last husband that died left her everything. Something to do with cattle or cattle trains or something. I never paid any attention. Speaking of attention, that 'cow of a woman' attempted to seduce me into sleeping with her in that ghastly round bed filled with her ugly poodles."

"Cut to the chase, Patrick," said Walter. "What happened in the last few days about your interior design work on the house that she bought?"

"Ha! I laugh at your words of 'interior design.' That woman has no taste other than for rich fatty meats and mounds of pasta on her plate. I was to design a respectable abode for some wealthy tourist to visit each year, a second home where he and his family might be surrounded by the comforts of his home back in the states. That woman demanded that everything be pink or wallpapered with her choice of paisley patterns. She ordered complete walls to be moved. Then she carpeted everything that wasn't nailed down. Mexico is a land of hard-worn surfaces etched with the dignity of thousands of feet abrading the surfaces through years of use. Not plush, loopy pastel carpeting wall to wall. She had my plans for a classical Greek entrance to the house destroyed. She is impossible, always harping on about what everything costs. Talent and divine objects cost money."

"You sound as if the venture is completely over," said Walter.

"Over? It never began! Not only has she had me locked out of my cottage at Las Brisas, depriving me of my belongings. She has listed the estate for sale in its half-finished condition for less than what she paid for it a week ago! The final blow was her intrusion into my cottage at the exact moment that Edwardo was relieving the constant nervous tension from my neck and back. I shan't repeat the indignities of her coarse guttural language. I know now that she was truly not a Lady of the English Court at all."

"I'll call the manager of Las Brisas in the morning and see if I can obtain his permission for Walter and me to gather your things from the cottage," I said. "What is the present state of your finances, Patrick? We have all survived in the past and will in the future."

"I have in my money belt approximately $14,000 pesos and $45 in US money. I was there when Lady Whittington signed me into Las Brisas. She verbally told the manager that I was her guest, so I won't owe any staggering amount for the few days of using the cottage. However, I will require the $14,000 pesos to complete the work on the condominium I bought. So far, I have committed to $2,500 pesos worth of improvements. My pesos should cover the cost, and I will put it back on the market and make a good profit. You'll see."

"Patrick, you are still short of money. Your pesos and the US $45 only amount to about $1,200 US, and you will be short an equal amount in paying for the improvements. Is there any way you can scale back on spending so much money on the apartment?"

"I have put a few marvelous paintings on hold at a gallery. I may lose my deposits, but that would cut the budget back considerably."

"Patrick, tonight is not the time to sit in our hotel room and mope about our circumstances. We have not eaten, and I assume you haven't either. You may select a suitable shirt from Walter's and my vast collection of plebeian clothing, anything to get you out of that herringbone jacket. I have promised Walter that I would accompany him back to his old stomping grounds at the El Colonial Hotel. After a good dinner and conversation with his old boss, Walter plans on engaging a few of the college rookies and relieve them of their holiday money over a game or two of shell and pea."

The three of us dined as we had in the past, all talking at once—good friends intent on helping each other out with any problems. Patrick even warned Walter of his excess of alcohol if he planned to fleece the college kids. At midnight, we rode a taxicab back to the hotel, where Walter entered the lobby first to check that no one saw Patrick enter as the third person to share our two-bed room. We shared one last nightcap as Walter counted his assortment of pesos and American money from the night's winnings.

"Well, how did you do, Walter?" asked Patrick.

"Better than I intended," he said. "I played nine games and purposely lost two of them when the number of players was small. That raked in the heavy rollers for the big kill. I mentally counted the incoming cash, and once I hit $2,000, I told Raub that it was time to make our exit."

"How did you two pull that one off without being beaten to death?"

"Raub comes up to the group as if he is going to place a bet. He watches the game, and before a new game begins, he acts as if he's about to place a bet but doesn't. Then he wins his Academy Award in acting by yelling in a loud voice, 'Put the cash away! Here comes security!' And we both run. The minute the kids see the two of us running, they panic and also run. Gambling in Mexico is illegal and has been since 1947, but they still have their underground gaming parlors, approved casinos, horseracing, and lottery. My game of shell and pea, like dominoes, dice, and pool, are legal, but the kids don't know that."

As always, Patrick was treated to his own bed, and Walter and I slept together in the other bed. It was like old times, the three of us... *compañeros!*

Chapter Twenty
The End of a Fine Romance

The following morning was like old times. It was a part of what the three of us did each morning: the race to use the bathroom first, the eager wait for a steaming pot of coffee delivered by room service, and the back and forth making plans for the day.

Naturally, Patrick was first to use the bathroom. He never failed to leave it in shambles. Without asking, he used my razor, my toothbrush, and toothpaste as well. I was allowed the use of the bathroom next. While tidying up the room, I noticed that Patrick's usual pile of soiled socks, underwear, t-shirt, and the shirt I loaned him the night before were nowhere to be seen. It was Walter who was known for his fastidious behavior when it came to clothing. Patrick never picked up after himself in his life. He disliked wearing the same garment for two consecutive days. Upon exiting the bathroom, I was not surprised to find Patrick wearing yet another of my clean shirts and a pair of my socks.

"You're welcome, Patrick," I said with a frosted tone. "At this moment, the clothing you saw in my dresser drawer is all I have to my name until I get back to Seattle. You are welcome to share with me what little I have left, but until I have secured your belongings from the locked cottage at Las Brisas, I suggest you launder your unmentionables as we do each night."

"Raub, I shall return your garments to you after being properly cleaned at a local laundry. I simply cannot wear the same article of clothing for a second day. It is so *gauche,* so *sauvage,* so *classe inférieure.*"

"We get your point, Patrick, but after Saturday, who is going to be around to pick up after you and keep you out of all these messes you seem to get into? I don't mean to infer that your Edwardo was a mess. On the contrary, I'm sure he was quite handsome and eager to relieve your neck tensions after a hard day of hobnobbing with Lady Whittington."

"Patrick, Raub and I have decided to pool our money with what you have left. Our airline tickets are paid for, and we have reserved enough money for the next few days of simple food and our hotel bill. We are willing to share the balance with you. I'll be all right once I hit San Francisco and my brother's place. Raub may not have his apartment back in Seattle anymore, but I think he only wants to go back to clear up a few leftover items and then head back to Honolulu. Raub and I will get by, but you will need all the help you can get. From what I've seen, the local real estate market is not a hot moneymaking operation here in Acapulco, especially in condominiums in the old part of town. Take it easy on what you are spending to redo it. Make a little profit, then get your ass back to the states. Go back to writing. That's what you do best."

"You're a fine one to give lectures on finances, Walter. For your information, I only have $1,000 applied to the purchase of the condominium, and I have nearly enough to pay for the improvements I have ordered."

"But by your own admission, you only have about $1,200 in your trusty money belt."

"That is why I must complete the condominium project as quickly as possible. Then sell it, make a tidy little profit, and use the money from the new owner to pay off the balance of what I owe on the purchase."

"Patrick, what if the condominium doesn't sell right away?" I said, "You must be paying the seller of the unit something in interest. What about the monthly costs to the apartment? Like electricity? gas? and water? I don't think you've thought this out, Patrick. Lady Whittington has the money for any kind of contingency that might arise, but you don't. I'm going to make the telephone call to the Las Brisas Hotel manager and persuade him to let Walter and me into your cottage to gather up your things. You, I think, should dash down to that art gallery, and finagle your way out of purchasing those paintings. Give them the old 'my wife has been taken seriously ill and may die, but I must take her back to the states for proper medical attention.' You know the routine, and I'm sure you have used it many times before."

We were successful in gathering up Patrick's belongings from the Las Brisas. The manager understood the problem. He had dealt with Lady Whittington several times in the past, and Patrick was not the first person she ordered locked out of their cottage.

"Señor Dennis thanks you for your assistance and has insisted that I present you with one of his autographed books as a special thank you for all that you have done."

"*Muchas gracias,* Señor Karr. I shall treasure it always."

It was Walter's hand that signed the name "Patrick Dennis" to the book while riding the taxicab to Las Brisas. The book, *Little Me, the Intimate Memoirs of that Great Star of Stage, Screen and Television, Belle Poitrine* was now tightly clutched in the manager's hands after he leafed through it, revealing an indelicate photograph of Miss Poitrine posing, *sans* costume, for her film *Paradise Lost.*

Patrick, Walter, and I met for a leisurely lunch. Unfortunately, Patrick was in a bad mood and snapped at us for no apparent reason.

"Patrick, we know this is a most trying time for you. Before we order our lunch, Walter and I want to support you in any way we can. We have pooled our funds, and barring any unforeseen circumstances like open-heart surgery, we have enough money to get us back to the states tomorrow. We are prepared to give you the balance of our funds and hope that you will use the money wisely in clearing up this mess you've gotten yourself into. The total is a little over $4,200."

Patrick sat stunned! He was speechless! An unusual state for Edward Everett Tanner III. He gathered up the sealed envelope in his trembling hand and gently kissed it. "I swear, you two are my closest and very dearest friends. I will never forget how you have cared for me. I shall pay you back every single penny of what you have spent on me."

We finished our lunches in silence.

"Now that you have retrieved my possessions, I had better check myself into a room here at the Fairmont. This hotel seems far away from Lady Whittington. I have some things to take care of, and I'm sure you two will start packing for your early morning flight tomorrow. We'll have drinks and dinner in my room tonight, sort of a *bon voyage* to our living together for all these long adventuresome months."

It was almost sunset when I asked the telephone operator to be connected to Señor Dennis's room, but she had no one registered by that name. "Try 'Tanner.' 'Dennis' is his book-writing name." But again, she had no one registered by that name.

"You don't suppose he registered, just to be funny, under the name of 'Roger Danbury,' do you?"

"I doubt it, Walter. I'm going down to the lobby to see if he left us a note."

There was no note, but a large cardboard box sat behind the desk with the names "Karr/Healy" jauntily written across the sealed flaps.

"What's in the box?" Walter asked.

"I would guess the remainder of the clothes that Patrick borrowed from me, but it certainly is heavier than what I would have expected."

Along with my clothing, the now battered Roger Danbury typewriter was at the bottom of the box. Three copies of *Genius,* two autographed copies of *Guestward Ho!* and a paperback copy of *Auntie Mame* filled the rest of the box.

"Where do you think he got hold of the paperback? You know how he detested the cheaper versions of his books. Walter, open the case of the typewriter."

"There's a note under the roller. What does it say?" Walter asked.

"Suddenly, I don't feel like going out, and if I ran into the Lord Byron of literature, Patrick Dennis, I'm afraid I'd smash him in the nose. At least he got one more good use out of the Roger Danbury typewriter. Strikeovers, stuck keys, and all!"

My dearesy two friends/s,

What can I say? I love You both so much an# will never be a ble to reclaim your trust an# friendship.

Today, with your gift of money, I realized the trea-sure I have had in living with the two of you.

I also realized, th e truth an#wisdom you have spoken ko me about how I am handling my life an# have made some very important decisions.

Contrary to what you might believe, I am a competent designer an# have excellent taste in all things artistically associated with interior design.

I never want to lift a pencil or write another word in a books. I am pursuing a career in interior design. Not here in this desolate qwasteland of ignorant impoverished people, but back where I belong / / / back in the states.

I shall condone your possible feelingss of the actions I am taking today. I am walking away from the oil paintings. They were ghastly cheap looking anyway.

I did heed your suggestion an# inquired as to teh monthly upkeep of my little condominium. Rented or not there Is a monthly charge of almost $900 US I went back to it this afternoon an# saw the error of my judgment in purchasing it. It will never sell an# probably nevebe rented out. It is, as you say in the wrong part of town. I have walked from thiobligation as well.

Forgive me* dear friends, I must go where my talents will be appreciated.

I am taking the afternoon airline to Houston, Texas.

Goodbye and good luck. It is only the two of you 'Campaneros' now.

Pastrick

Patrick stole stationery from every hotel he ever stayed in during his lifetime. His hastily typed note was on The Plaza Hotel stationery.

I folded the two-page letter and placed it along with the other items in the box in my duffle bag. "Well, Walter, we arrived almost two years ago in fine style aboard the SS Caprice. Here we are going home in lesser style. I think I have about 285 pesos in my pocket. That's about $18. You must have about the same. I'm so glad it's all over, the adventure with Patrick and all. I'm also glad that you are going home to San Francisco and settle the affairs of your father with your brother. You're probably right. I will end up back in Honolulu, but until then, if you ever feel like coming back to Seattle for a visit, give a call. I'll be there until I can build up my nest egg once again. You're lucky, you've still got your shells and pea game."

Chapter Twenty-One
Life Without the Muse

I can't tell you how many times I tried to muster up the courage to call Patrick's agent in New York City. Or even his generous publisher who, by this time, had washed his hands of ever getting another book of pure wit from Patrick Dennis.

He had disappeared from the face of the earth.

Walter returned to San Francisco and settled out his father's affairs. He lived for a while in his father's apartment in San Mateo, a suburb south of San Francisco. But he soon found he was spending more and more time in the city, so he rented an apartment there. Unfortunately, Walter was not a letter writer, and I found it difficult to reach him by phone.

I called Juanita one Sunday afternoon. It was Juanita's one day of rest when she invited friends to come aboard the boat, talk, drink, and eat. "Honey, I ain't seen Walter in over four months. The last telephone number I had for him has been disconnected now for a month or two. You know Walter. If he had moved, the first thing he would do is get his telephone working again. He can't live without a telephone. I hate the blasted things. Well, I'm worried about him too. You know Walter. One minute he's high on the hog, and the next he could be at death's door. The last time I saw him, he was with that fellow you two hooked up with on that Mexican boat trip ... Patrick something. The real funny one who sang, remember?"

"I sure do, Juanita, and that's another one I would like to get back in touch with. I'm leaving Seattle and moving back to Honolulu. I think I'll stop over in San Francisco and see if I can find Walter and maybe get a lead on Patrick Dennis at the same time."

A month later, I was at the Sheraton Palace and had left word with Walter's brother about where I was and why I was in town. So we met for lunch the following day. That's when I found out what had happened to Walter.

"Things got pretty out of hand for Walter," his brother said. "He just can't hold his liquor anymore. He's drunk all the time. I even got him a roommate to watch out for him, but he moved out, said he couldn't take it anymore. So I put Walter in rehab, but that didn't work either."

"Can I go see him?" I asked.

"I don't know where he is and won't until Dad's place closes escrow. We sold all the furniture from Dad's apartment and his car. Hell, Walter went through that money in about a month. I got a letter from a guy named Edward Tanner who's been looking for Walter like we have for several months now. He seemed to know a lot about Walter and his problem. I've got his address here someplace."

Patrick's address was written on a postcard advertising the opening of a limited showing/sale of a Jackson Pollock painting at a gallery in Houston on March 7, 1971. The picture on the postcard was ablaze with brilliant colors that had been splashed with vigorous force onto a blank canvas as it hung defenseless on a wall. The painting was entitled "Contentious Bitch" and was offered for sale at $75,000.

Patrick's inked note was brief and less alarming.

"Have Walter call me. *Muy importante!* – EVT, III"

I read the faint postal cancellation mark on the card as September 22nd. I mentally made a note to ask Patrick how the opening for the Pollock painting had gone if I ever ran into him again.

The Houston gallery's telephone rang and rang but was never answered. On the postcard, a map below the gallery's address showed a large, curved arrow pointing to the Epperson Building. After further inquiries, I talked to Lawrence Singleton Epperson, whose Texas drawl was as long as his name. "Well, Ah don't rightly know. Yah see, the gallery jist up an' closed one weekend. Lotsa' people comin' intah my store tah find out where ever'body went. Then this guy by the name a Adrius Wolfmonger got all steamed up an' huffy 'bout gettin' his paintins' back an' called the police. Them boys, along with Mr. Dennis, sure caused a lotta' bad feelins.'"

"Bad feelins" wasn't all that Patrick and his partners in the gallery cooked up that year. The gallery, its contents, records, and what few accounting books they could find were snatched up by the courts when complaints of fraud and thievery were brought to the attention of the Houston Police Department.

I can't testify to the validity of the following facts. However, what I was told had happened in Houston speaks volumes about Patrick Dennis's frame of mind. Apparently, upon Patrick's arrival in Houston from Acapulco, he checked into the Shamrock Hotel, located in the "wrong part of town."

I'm sure that Patrick was drawn to the hotel by the Irish references, i.e., Shamrock, St. Patrick, McCarthy, the Irishman who built it, green staff uniforms, and even signing the hotel register in green ink. He registered as Edward Everett Tanner III.

Patrick reinvented himself again. He had over $5,000 in his pocket. So Patrick set off on a new adventure with new clothing, a mustache, a pointed beard, and alligator luggage.

Maxine Mesinger, nicknamed "Miss Moonlight," wrote a celebrity gossip column in the *Houston Chronicle*. She took up residence in the Shamrock Hotel in 1965. To fill her column and provide scintillating gossip to her weekly television audience, Maxine struck a deal with the Shamrock Hotel. She was alerted of any Hollywood stars or influential businessmen visiting the hotel.

The name of Edward Everett Tanner III crossed Maxine's desk the day he checked into the Shamrock. She must have wondered who this Edward Everett Tanner III was. He used a smart Upper East Side townhouse address on 91st street as a home reference. A few long-distance telephone calls gave her all the information she needed for an item in the *Houston Chronicle*. The hilariously funny creator of *Auntie Mame*—the book and now the movie—was residing at the Shamrock Hotel.

Before she got her scoop in the paper, I'm sure that at their first meeting, Patrick mesmerized Maxine as she provided him with the names of influential local people who would help him withdraw from his world of notoriety and away from the name of Patrick Dennis. Edward Everett Tanner III used the name Patrick Dennis when it served a lucrative purpose. Now his birth name was also betraying his quest for anonymity.

With her Rolodex of influential old Houston ladies needing someone to brighten up their dinner parties, Maxine introduced them to Clifton Webmaster, Jr., née Patrick. At such a glittering *soirée*, "Clifton," née Patrick, met the two owners of the Houston art gallery after finishing a rip-roaring monologue on the life of Jackson Pollock and the artist's wife, Lee Krasner.

Patrick fell into the tangled web of the gallery owners, who were not above fraud and duplicity when selling their worthless paintings. There was no formal contract signed, only a verbal agreement with Patrick. By now, he had confessed his real identity to his two new partners. This innocent act would eventually add his name to the gallery's bankruptcy, and other charges.

Patrick let slip to Maxine that a rare and valuable Jackson Pollock painting had been placed in the gallery on consignment. The 8-ft. by 10-ft. unframed painting was entitled *"Contentious Bitch."* Word spread around the Houston art world that Pollock, before his death, named the picture after Peggy Guggenheim, his separated wife, Lee Krasner, or his current mistress Ruth Kligman. Whoever inspired Pollock's abstract expressionist paint dribbles, the painting sold!

Patrick, aware of copyright laws, infringements, and unauthorized use of images of the painting, steadfastly refused to allow the press even one photograph of the picture.

"That's a matter for the Jackson Pollack Estate," he explained.

The catered affair at the Shamrock Hotel brought out several luminaries to unveil the fake Pollock painting. Most notably, Ambassador Stanton Griffis, who Patrick serenaded royally with his Africa, Egypt, and Spain stories. I'm sure that Patrick stressed the words "served and stationed" when speaking of these locations, knowing that Griffis had served as the American Ambassador to Egypt, Spain, Poland, and Argentina, before retiring.

Griffis lived in numerous homes and traveled extensively. He needed a competent butler, or "man to take charge" of his houses and the entertainment of political guests. Without informing his partners in the gallery, Patrick accepted the position. He instructed Stanton Griffis to call him "Edwards."

Patrick was particular about names and favored those that ended in "s." "The 's' sound remains on the tongue as you say words like 'laborious' or the name of 'Lucius Licinius Lucullus.' Can't you hear it? Of the thousands and thousands of words in the English language, very few end in 's' unless you make the word plural."

Adrius Wolfmonger, the unsuspecting artist whose painting had been purposely mislabeled as a "Jackson Pollack," tried to retrieve his paintings from the now-closed gallery. He notified the Houston Police Department. Mr. Epperson, the building owner, cooperated with the police. At the same time, Adrius Wolfmonger packed his remaining pieces of abstract art and returned to Beaumont, Texas, and the Jefferson County Department of Roads.

After an extensive investigation into the Jackson Pollock 8-ft. by 10-ft. abstract work of art by a trusted gallery in New York City, the new owner received the distressing news that it was a fake. Private investigators and attorneys swarmed the Epperson Building and questioned anyone who might know the perpetrators of this hoax. The name of Patrick Dennis never came up, only Edward Tanner, and no address was available for his whereabouts.

When Louise first heard of Edward Tanner's involvement in a Jackson Pollock painting hoax, she dismissed the similarity of names. She still believed that Patrick was living comfortably somewhere in Mexico. However, friends had seen the article about the fraud in the local East Hampton, Long Island newspaper and brought it to Louise's attention. She called her good friend, Peggy Guggenheim, to ask about the story.

In my time with Patrick, he never embraced the avant-garde, either with art or music. If the art was not Romanesque, classical, or highly refined by a respected master, he considered it uncouth or barbarian. For example, Patrick's condemnation of the Beatles' hit song, "She Loves You, Yeah, Yeah, Yeah," was, "What it lacks in pure musical organization and thought, it makes up for in the use of nonsensical rubbish for words."

The bankruptcy of the three owners of the defunct art gallery, of which Patrick, under the name Edward Tanner, was one, fouled the legal system of Houston for years. The swindled owner of the phony Jackson Pollock painting hung it on the wall of his four-car garage to remind himself of his folly of buying art without first researching its authenticity.

Edwards, Edward Everett Tanner III's new incarnation, was now what he once thought he could never live without... a butler.

Chapter Twenty-Two

It's So Hard Getting Good Help These Days

Ambassador Griffis was not a healthy man, and due to his illness and being confined to bed, there was little that Patrick could do for him. There were no grand royal receptions of political or diplomatic guests. No evening galas to organize. In fact, Stanton Griffis was about to be transferred from his twenty-four-room mansion in West Palm Beach into a caregiving facility where he would eventually die.

Patrick once confessed to Walter that he categorized socialites and well-to-do people first by how gregarious they were, then by intelligence, and last, how much money they had. Patrick despised those committed to being unintelligent. Those who had no desire for learning or any ambition to improve themselves. A simple housecleaner who could barely speak English could reveal her deepest emotions to Patrick about wanting to succeed in her position. Patrick had tremendous compassion for other people's feelings and his own. Maybe that's why I never understood his actions in Acapulco all those years ago. When he used my money to pay a hotel bill for *Estancia*, the prostitute who befriended him in his hour of need.

Nancy Morgan Runnells, the wife of businessman Clive Runnells, interviewed "Edwards" for the job of a butler. His references were typed on the full-color embossed stationery of the US embassy in Buenos Aires,

Argentina. He was highly recommended by the Honorable Stanton Griffis. At the time, Patrick was unaware that the principal residence of the Runnells was Houston, Texas. He was greatly relieved to find that his services were to be performed at the Runnells' Lake Forest, Illinois home, and their apartment in New York City. But working as a butler for the Runnells didn't work out, and Patrick began compiling a list of likely new families he could work for.

Joan Kroc was his first choice. The effervescent, lively Joan and "Edwards," hit it off. Joan was gregarious, talented, beautiful, and loved to laugh about anything, even herself. She had a heart of gold that belonged to her second husband, Ray Kroc, CEO of McDonald's. He had found her playing piano and singing at a cocktail bar in Minnesota. They shared a secret romance for over twelve years before divorcing their respective spouses and marrying in 1969.

Living with a wealthy man like Ray Kroc was a new experience for Joan. "Edwards" helped her deal with her new moneyed lifestyle, e.g., if she was about to make a social mistake. As a result, Joan refused to travel for even one night without "Edwards."

Ray Kroc also appreciated "Edwards." The butler even participated in cooking exploratory new versions of French fries and McDonald's hamburgers, the source of the billionaire's wealth.

Patrick/Edwards had completed his last book, *3-D,* while working for the Runnells. Still, following its publication, Patrick did not reveal his authorship to either Joan or Ray Kroc.

In 1975, Walter called me in Hawaii. He casually mentioned that he had recently spent a long drunken weekend with Patrick in San Francisco. Apparently, Patrick had escorted Joan Kroc to San Francisco for several days of McDonald's meetings and to see her off on a two-week getaway to Tokyo.

Walter filled me in on all of Patrick's happenings and escapades. Finally, he let the cat out of the bag about Patrick's sudden illness.

The two of them had gone to Juanita's for drinks and dinner. That's when Patrick became violently ill at the table and began coughing up blood. Patrick had mentioned several times that he thought he had a bad ulcer. Years of cigarettes, heavy drinking, and poor food choices didn't help.

Ray Kroc canceled his planned meeting in San Francisco, and Patrick joined him in the Kroc's San Diego home. On hearing of "Edwards'" illness, Joan flew back to join them. Unfortunately, none of the doctors at Scripps or UCLA could diagnose what was wrong with Patrick. He was told to rest for a couple of weeks.

Patrick promised to stay in touch, but neither Walter nor I heard from Patrick for several months. Finally, Walter joined me in Hawaii, but his drinking problem was far too advanced for him to secure or maintain employment. In the meantime, Patrick continued to buttle for the Krocs. He occasionally suffered abdominal pains and loss of appetite. His weight loss continued. The doctors had no answer for his illness.

Patrick finally confessed to Joan his real identity. He also informed her about his checkered past and that he must resign and return to New York City to be with his wife and children. Joan accompanied him to New York City in the McDonalds' corporate jet. At this point in his life—now fifty-five years of age—Patrick had few personal possessions. He didn't even own one copy of any of the sixteen novels he had written.

Patrick returned to the open arms of Louise and his two children and was diagnosed with pancreatic cancer. The prognosis was that he had only weeks to live. Unable to face the reality of his illness and upcoming death, Patrick revisited his vast wardrobe of treasured English suits, shoes, bowlers, and walking canes. Alone, he retraced his favorite haunts and spent two drunken days living in Central Park. Now, having accepted his pending death, Patrick sought comfort from Louise. He spent his last few weeks lovingly cared for by his family. His death was long and painful.

On November 6, 1976, Patrick died while napping in Louise's bed. Some have reported there was no obituary, nor even a news item, in the newspaper announcing his death. Instead, Patrick was cremated without ceremony.

After numerous battles with Walter, he agreed to return to San Francisco and seek help with the aid of his brother. I helped him clear out his tiny apartment in Waikiki. He, like Patrick, had few possessions. One suitcase of assorted clothing. The only remaining items to be removed from his apartment were hundreds of liquor bottles hidden under the bed, behind the draperies, and in clothes closets. I had a feeling that I would never see Walter again. Walter, the epitome of ultra-smart taste in his wardrobe, left Honolulu in soiled, stained Bermuda shorts and a clean but un-ironed shirt.

A mutual friend wrote me several months later that Walter's body had been found in a Castro area apartment. He had died several days before. The autopsy ruled that he had died of liver cirrhosis and extreme dehydration. He had no stomach contents at the time of his death.

Louise Stickney Tanner died on May 15, 2000, in the same bed as Patrick had all those years before. Her two children, Michael and Elizabeth, and a host of friends attended her funeral. Nestled within her arms was the urn of ashes of her late husband, Patrick Dennis—Edward Everett Tanner III.

Now, nearly fifty years after first meeting Patrick, I re-read my cherished letters and notes from him. Some bring laughter—others bring tears. I will never know whether it was something I had said or done that ended our close friendship. Maybe he just tired of Walter and me, and it was time to reinvent himself once more.

It doesn't really matter. What does matter is the fact that I knew him.

Walter Healey

About The Author

Robert Karr
30 December, 1934 – 15 March, 2017

After serving several years with Rogers & Cowan as a public relations agent in Beverly Hills, Calif., representing 1960s television and motion picture clientele, Robert returned to his favorite home, Hawaii, and continued his career in broadcasting.

Robert worked with and for such greats as Dick Van Dyke, Cara Williams, Jack Benny, Raymond Burr, Gladys Cooper, Gail Patrick Jackson, Gig Young, Charles Boyer, and held the distinction of being the first boss to hire (and fire) a determined high school songstress by the name of Bette Midler. Some of Robert's clients became lifelong friends, no mean feat in Hollywood.

Besides his volumes of memoirs, Robert wrote fiction based on his beloved interests, namely the beauty and fascinating history of Hawaii and his favorite animal, cats.

Robert was in various stages of editing six of his novels including *LaMort du'u Requiro—The Death of a Shark*, another entitled *Yah Did Too*, written completely in dialogue, no narrative, in preparation for publication. His library of work includes a Western screenplay.

His short story "A Hawaiian Encounter," was published in *Palm Springs Life Magazine*.

About Bernie Ardia

Having a 40-year career as a theatrical hair designer and wig builder this California native started in print work and television, commercials, and television specials such as *Happy Birthday Hollywood*. Ardia returned to live theater with David Merrick's national tour of *42nd St*. After many years of touring with live productions such as Chita Rivera's *Can-Can*, Tim Curry's *Me and My Girl*, *Showboat*, he then focused on designing hair for productions of Eleanor Bergstein's *Dirty Dancing*, *Kiss of the Spider Woman*, the Kennedy Center's *Ragtime*, Cameron Mackintosh's *Oliver*, *Elf*, and *Starlight Express* at the Las Vegas Hilton among others. Ardia has now designed for well over 75 productions. Though he semi-retired to allow more time for writing, productions still have his designs onstage today. As a child, after seeing Barbra Streisand open for Liberace in Las Vegas, he followed her career as a hobby—turning that into a book, *Barbra Streisand in New York City*. For the last several years he has been working on a biography of Streisand's stepfather. That work was delayed for three years after Patrick Dennis landed on his desk. Falling in love with this adventurous tale he dedicated his time to see it through to publication so this wonderful 'slice of a life' story could be shared.

As a 'Dreamer' he always sees ideas as possible. Most of Ardia's life expectations have been surpassed. He is proud to have worked with many talented performers and directors in his career including Hal Prince, Chita Rivera, Melody Thomas Scott, Jeanne Cooper, Eartha Kitt, George Wendt, Linda Carter, Molly Ringwald, Patrick Cassidy, Debbie Gibson, Anita Gillette, Pat Harrington, Michelle Lee, Carole Cook, Kathie Lee Gifford, Sally Ann Howe, Toni Tennille, John Schuck, Mackenzie Phillips, Constance Towers, Jamie Lynn Sigler, and more. Ardia now divides his time between Rancho Mirage, California, with constant traveling. Presenting *At Sea with Patrick Dennis: My Madcap Mexican Adventure with the Author of Auntie Mame* is another of his dreams come true.

9 781955 826259